Introductory Meats

Laboratory Manual

4th Edition

F.C. Parrish, Jr.

S. M. Lonergan

B. R. Wiegand

Paladin House of the Farley Court of Publishers

Publishers Row

Zenda WI 53195-0123

Acknowledgements

From: 3rd Edition: Dr. Parrish expresses his appreciation to Elisabeth Huff, Bob Johnson, Becky Thiel, and Bryon Wiegand, four very distinguished teaching assistants for their help in revising the manual.

4th Edition: The authors acknowledge Sherry Olsen, Kyle Grubbs, Aaron Fritchen, Justin Rickard and Hannah Evans for their assistance in the preparation of this revision.

Permission to Publish

Figure 4. Reproductions are courtesy of the U.S. Department of Agriculture

Figures 2, 3, 4, 6, 17, 18, 19, 20, 21, 22, 23, 24, 25, and 28 are used with the permission of the National Livestock and Meat Board.

Figures 7, 8, 9, 10, and 11. Courtesy of the National Pork Board.

Figure 26 and 27. Source: USDA Agriculture Marketing Service. Agriculture Handbook No. 31.

Figure 29. Used with permission from Kansas State University

Figure 30-36. Source: University of Illinois College of Agriculture, Agriculture Experiment Station, Bulletin 715.

Source of retail cuts of beef , pork and lamb cuts (Chapters V, VI, and VII). Uniform Retail Meat Identity Standards, National Livestock and Meat Board.

ISBN 978-0-88252-216-6

TABLE OF CONTENTS

I. DEFINITIONS OF TERMS

GENERAL TERMS

A. <u>Market Animal Evaluation Class</u> – Usually consists of four market animals varying in fatness, muscling, and quality. Live weights are given, but other quantitative and qualitative market animal characteristics are based on visual appraisal. Evaluators will estimate fatness, muscling, and quality characteristics. These estimates will be scored according to actual carcass data.

B. <u>Carcass Evaluation Class</u> – Usually consists of four carcasses from the live animal evaluation class viewed in a previous class period. Carcasses will be ribbed to expose rib/loin eyes. Yield and quality grade factors will be collected and data will be provided to each participant. These actual carcass measurements will be used as the basis for scoring your market animal estimates.

C. <u>Ribbing</u> – Cutting across the *longissimus* between the 12th and 13th ribs of beef and lamb carcasses and the 10th and 11th ribs of pork carcasses to expose rib/loin eyes.

D. <u>Cutability</u> – Ratio of retail cut weight (trimmed, boned, or partially boned) to the carcass that is salable as trimmed (boned or partially boned) retail cuts. Yield grade 1 beef and lamb carcasses would have a high cutability whereas yield grade 5 would have a low cutability.

E. <u>Yield Grades (YG)</u> – Beef and lamb carcasses are assigned cutability numbers 1, 2, 3, 4, and 5. A YG 1 represents the highest cutability and 5 signifies the lowest cutability carcass. USDA yield grades are based on actual data including fat thickness, ribeye area, kidney, pelvic, and heart fat, and hot carcass weight for beef. Yield grades for lambs are based only on fat thickness. Yield grades (U.S. 1, 2, 3, 4, and Utility) for pork carcasses are based on last rib fat thickness and ham muscling score and are used primarily for price reporting purposes by government agencies since most pork in the U.S. is sold on a lean percentage basis. The utility grade is based on poor quality, usually soft and oily lean, thin belly, and pale or dark lean.

F. <u>Quality</u> – Those desired characteristics of lean, fat, and bones associated with palatability, acceptability, and marketability.

G. <u>Quality Grades (QG)</u> – For beef and lamb carcasses quality grades are used to predict expected palatability (eating) characteristics of meat. These are based on degree of marbling (beef) or flank streaking (lamb) and stage of maturity. The USDA quality grades for carcasses from young beef are Prime, Choice, Select, Standard and Utility, and for lamb carcasses are Prime, Choice, Good, and Utility. U.S. Consumer grades of poultry are U.S. Grade A, B, and C.

H. <u>Leanness</u> – Ratio of total muscle to total fat.

I. <u>Muscling</u> – Ratio of total muscle to total bone.

1

J. Meatiness – Ratio of total muscle (M) plus acceptable fat (AF) to total bone (TB) plus trimmable fat (TF).

K. Trimmable Fat – That fat which exceeds the maximum level which could be sold on a retail cut of meat.

L. Dressing Percent (sometimes referred to as yield) – is defined as:

$$\frac{\text{Hot Carcass Weight} \times 100}{\text{Live Weight}}$$

M. Wholesale (Primal) Cut - Large cuts of meat from a carcass, e.g. chuck, loin, leg.

N. Subprimal – Smaller cuts made from primal, e.g., short loin, sirloin.

O. Retail – Meat cuts sold at retail usually fabricated from primal and sub-primals, e.g., rib steak, loin chop, rump roast.

P. Boxed Beef – Beef primal/subprimal packed in vacuum bags and placed in a cardboard box.

SPECIFIC TERMS

A. Quality Terms

1. Color – usually refers to the color of the lean observed in the ribeyes of beef and lamb carcasses and loin eyes of pork carcasses; between ribs or in the flanks of pork and lamb carcasses, in the lumbar lean and face of the ham of pork carcasses, and in the cut surface of beef wholesale cuts and pork hams. It is also a major quality factor. The desirable color of beef, pork, and lamb cut surfaces is described as cherry-red, reddish pink, and pinkish-red, respectively. Undesirable (dark, light, or two-toned) lean color or a carcass or a cut results in discounting that particular carcass or cut. Color can also refer to the color of subcutaneous fat. A white fat is preferable to a yellow fat cover. Indeed, yellow fat of beef carcasses will result in a large discount in carcass value.

2. Marbling - flecks of fat (intramuscular fat) within the lean, observed in the ribeyes of beef and lamb carcasses and loin eyes of pork carcasses and the cut surfaces of beef wholesale cuts and pork hams. It is a major quality factor which is visually or camera assessed in the ribbed carcasses. Marbling has three major components: amount or degree, texture (fineness or coarseness), and distribution of pieces. All three of these components need to be taken into consideration in judging and grading beef carcasses, but primary emphasis is placed on amount or degree. The degrees of marbling from least to most in beef carcasses are practically devoid, traces, slight, small, modest, moderate, slightly abundant, moderately abundant, and abundant. These degrees of marbling correspond to USDA quality grades.

3. <u>Maturity</u> – age of the carcass or cut as determined by the physiological appearance of bone and cartilage. It is a factor of importance in lamb and beef quality grading. There are four general maturity group classifications.

   a. Very young is the most youthful maturity group. It is characterized by very red and porous bone and the redness is displayed in the entire rib or in the feather bone. Buttons are always present and they are very soft and easily dented.

   b. Young is the second maturity group. It is characterized by red and porous bone, but slight evidence of the disappearance of the redness in the ribs and feather bones. Buttons are always present and they are soft and easily dented.

   c. Intermediate is the third maturity group. It is characterized by only slight redness in the rib and feather bones. Buttons are always present, but they may show slight evidences of ossification. The buttons are not always easily dented.

   d. Mature is the oldest maturity group. It is characterized by hard, white, flinty feather bones and ribs lacking redness. Buttons are seldom distinguished but rather appear as ossified tips of the feather bone.

4. <u>Buttons</u> - soft, white cartilaginous tips on the dorsal edge of the feather bones of young carcasses. These buttons change from cartilage to bone as an animal matures (see Figure 3).

5. <u>Cervical vertebrae</u> – vertebrae of the backbone anterior to the thoracic vertebrae. The first cervical vertebra is commonly called the atlas joint. This is the location of head removal in the slaughter operation (see Figure 3).

6. <u>Thoracic vertebrae</u> – vertebrae of the backbone anterior to the lumbar vertebrae and posterior to the cervical vertebrae. The maturity of the 9-12 thoracic vertebrae are extremely important in beef grading as the grader pays close attention to the stage of maturity of these vertebrae, especially between the interface of B (young) and C (old) maturity where the largest carcass value price discounts usually occur (see Figure 3).

7. <u>Lumbar vertebrae</u> - vertebrae of the backbone posterior to the last thoracic vertebrae (last rib) and just anterior to the sacral vertebrae. They are useful in determining carcass maturity, especially between B and C maturity beef carcasses (see Figure 3).

8. <u>Sacral vertebrae</u> – vertebrae of the backbone posterior to the lumbar vertebrae. They are used also in determining maturity of a carcass. These vertebrae are the first to ossify (see Figure 3).

9. <u>Feather bones</u> – split spinous processes extending dorsally from the thoracic vertebrae (backbones).

10. <u>Chine bones</u> – bodies of cervical, thoracic, lumbar, and sacral vertebrae.

11. <u>Firmness</u> – the straight edged appearance of the cut surface of rib and loin eyes and wholesale cuts. Also, it refers to freedom of muscle separation or sagging in wholesale cuts. Firmness of non-ribbed lamb and pork carcasses is determined by flank resistance to handling. Firmness of flank varies with maturity and fatness. It is used as a quality indicator.

12. <u>Texture</u> – texture is the coarseness or fineness of the grain of the lean as observed in rib and loin eyes and cut surfaces. Fine texture appears smooth and shiny to the eye; whereas, coarse texture appears ridged and dull in appearance. Fine texture is associated with tenderness. It is a quality indicating characteristic.

13. <u>Flank lacing or streaking</u> – fat within and upon the lean tissue in the flank region of lamb carcasses. It is an important quality factor in grading and evaluating lamb carcasses. Certain degrees are required to meet the USDA grades of Choice and Prime.

14. <u>Feathering</u> – fine streaks of fat intermingled with the lean between the ribs (intercostal muscles) of beef, lamb, pork or veal carcasses.

15. <u>Break joint</u> – evidence of youthfulness in lamb carcasses. It is the rough or jagged edge at the site of removal of the fore shank of lamb used to differentiate lamb from mutton carcasses. Lamb carcasses must have one break joint to qualify for the lamb carcass grades. This is opposed to a spool joint (looks like a spool) found on yearling lamb and mutton carcasses in which the break joint has ossified and the foreshank must be removed at the spool joint (see Figure 9).

16. <u>Aitch bone</u> – the split pelvic (ischium) bone of beef, veal, and pork carcasses.

B. Fat

1. <u>Backfat</u> – deposit of subcutaneous (outside) fat over the back of a carcass. The amount of backfat on a carcass is an excellent means of determining the percentage of trimmed retail cuts.

2. <u>Backfat thickness</u> – usually thought of as an average of three measurements of backfat in pork carcasses taken opposite the first rib, last rib, and last lumbar vertebrae. It is a strong direct measurement of carcass fatness and has a strong inverse relationship with carcass leanness.

3. <u>Fat thickness over the ribeye</u> – measured three-fourths the length of the ribeye starting from the chine side and extending laterally between the 12th and 13th ribs in beef carcasses. It is measured at the midpoint of a ribeye between the 12th and 13th ribs of a lamb carcass. An important measurement made in determining beef and lamb yield grades.

4. <u>Fat thickness over the loin eye</u> – measured three fourths of the length of the loin eye starting from the chine side and extending laterally between the 10th

and 11th ribs in pork carcasses. An excellent direct measurement of carcass fatness, and a strong, inverse relationship to muscling.

5. <u>Lower rib/body wall thickness</u> – total thickness of the body wall to include fat, lean, and bone in lamb carcasses. It is measured five inches from the midline at the 12th and 13th rib interface curvilinear to the rib cage.

6. <u>Seam</u> <u>fat</u> – deposits of fat between muscles (intermuscular fat). Usually observed in wholesale cuts (especially the chuck in beef or shoulder in pork and lamb carcasses) and large amounts are undesirable.

7. <u>Overflow fat</u> – fat covering over the ribs (ventral location) on the inside of a beef, lamb, pork, or veal carcass. Large amounts are undesirable.

8. <u>Udder</u> <u>fat</u> – it is the deposit of fat in the mammary region of a female carcass. It can be distinguished from cod fat because it contains mammary tissue and appears smooth. Excessive amounts are undesirable.

9. <u>Cod fat</u> – it is the deposit of fat in the scrotum region of a male carcass. It has a rough appearance. Excessive amounts are undesirable.

10. <u>Fat collar</u> – deposit of fat over the lower inside portion (ventral) of the cushion of a ham or round.

11. <u>Kidney, pelvic and heart (KPH) fat</u> – deposits of internal fat.
    a. Kidney fat (K) is the fat surrounding the kidney.
    b. Pelvic fat (P) is deposits of fat in the pelvic area. KPH as a percent of a hot carcass weight of a beef is part of the adjustment of beef yield grade. KP is removed from lamb carcasses at the time of slaughter.
    c. Heart fat (H) is deposits of fat in the heart area.
    d. Leaf fat is deposits of fat surrounding the kidney of pork carcasses. It is removed from the carcass after evisceration has been completed during slaughter operations.

C. Muscling
    1. <u>Eye muscle</u> – the large major muscle (longissimus) along the backbone found in the ribeyes, loin eyes, and in the rib and loin cuts. It is evaluated for quality attributes (marbling, color, firmness, and texture), muscling (ribeye area) and trimness (fat depth opposite the eye).
    2. <u>Cushion</u> – the thick, plump, meaty portion of ham, leg, or round. It has length, width, thickness and plumpness dimensions. Bulge, fullness, and plumpness are synonymous terms describing a dimension of the bulging and meaty portion of a ham, leg, or round (side opposite the flank side). Sometimes used synonymously with center section.
    3. <u>Lean cuts (pork)</u> – ham, loin, Boston butt, and picnic shoulder. Percentage four lean cuts of a U.S. No. 1 carcass should be at least 60 percent of the carcass. A high percentage of four lean cuts is a very desirable attribute of a pork carcass.

4. Clod – thick, fleshy muscle lying over the forearm on the chuck of a beef carcass and a wholesale beef chuck.
5. Center section – the center section (portion) of the ham which extends from the aitch bone through the meaty portion of the ham to the shank. It is the most valuable part of the ham.
6. Lumbar lean – lean tissue or muscle (gluteus medius) found between the lumbar-sacral vertebra junction and the backfat on a pork carcass. It is used as an index of muscling in the absence of an exposed loineye.

D. Sex Identification
1. Cod and Udder fat – previously mentioned on page 5
2. Pizzle eye – it is the white disc-like tissue immediately behind the aitch bone from which the penis was removed from the carcass. It is used to distinguish steer and bull from heifer carcasses.
3. Gracilis muscle – it is the muscle adjacent to the aitch bone which is bean-shaped in heifer carcasses and diamond-shaped in steers.

E. Carcass Length
1. Carcass length – measured only in pork carcasses. Length of carcass is measured from the anterior edge of the first rib to the anterior edge of the aitch bone.

F. Processing terms
1. Color value – a number used to describe color of a sausage emulsion. The higher the number the more red the mixture.
2. Bind value – a number to indicate the capacity of a meat to bind water. The higher the value the higher the capacity to bind.
3. M:P – moisture to protein ratio is an important legal requirement in the manufacture of dry and semi-dry sausages.
4. Casing – natural or synthetic packages used to enclose sausages.
5. Emulsion – a colloidal system in which a liquid is dispersed (dispersed phase) in droplets of another liquid (the continuous phase) with which it is immiscible. An example of an oil-in-water emulsion is mayonnaise. An example of a water-in-oil emulsion is butter. Sausage batters are sometimes referred to as emulsions, but this is not an accurate description.
6. Nitrite – Sodium nitrite is a key ingredient in cured meat. Sodium nitrite is the source of nitric oxide. Nitric oxide is the essential component in forming the cured pigment form, nitrosohemochrome. Nitrite prevents warmed-over flavor, and inhibits the growth of *Clostridium botulinum.*
7. Sodium chloride – (table salt) is used in fresh and processed meats to improve water holding capacity, shelf life, and sensory quality.
8. Sodium phosphates – inorganic compounds used to improve processing functionality of meat proteins. Generally these compounds improve

myofibrillar protein solubility. Alkaline phosphates are used to improve water holding capacity of meat products. Acid phosphates are generally used to accelerate the curing reaction.

9. <u>Sodium erythorbate or sodium ascorbate</u> – reducing agents used in the development and stabilization of cured meat color.

10. <u>Sugar</u> – used as a sweetener in the curing mix, usually sucrose. The sugar, dextrose, is used as a source of simple carbohydrate for lactic acid production.

11. <u>Starter Culture</u> – lactic acid producing microorganism used in fermented sausage manufacture.

12. <u>Thermal Processing Unit</u> – a heat, smoke, and humidity controlled unit for thermally processing sausages and whole/boned meat cuts.

13. <u>Comminuted</u> – particle size reduction of meat by grinding and/or chopping.

14. <u>Pickle (Brine)</u> – a solution of salt, sugar and nitrite for curing meat. It may also contain sodium ascorbate/erythorbate and phosphates.

15. <u>Injection</u> – reference to the mechanical pressurized injection of a curing solution into meat cuts (i.e. hams, bellies).

16. <u>Stuffing</u> – introduction of comminuted meat into a casing by using sausage stuffing equipment.

17. <u>Vacuum Bag (package)</u> – a type of packaging material preventing oxygen transmission.

18. <u>90:10 trim</u> – cuts of meat having 90 parts lean and 10 parts fat by weight.

19. <u>50:50 trim</u> – cuts of meat having 50 parts lean and 50 parts fat by weight.

20. <u>Grinder</u> – mechanical equipment used to reduce particle size of cuts of meat using grinder plates with varying hold sizes to produce desired level of fineness or coarseness.

21. <u>Chopper</u> – mechanical equipment used to finely mince (chop) lean and fat to produce a stable batter (emulsion) for production of bologna or frankfurter.

22. <u>Mixer</u> – equipment used to uniformly distribute non-meat ingredients, i.e., spices, cure, etc. with comminuted meats.

23. <u>Spices</u> – non-meat ingredients used solely as flavorings (e.g., pepper, garlic, sage, onion powder) in processed meat products.

24. <u>Brine</u> – a solution of high purity salt in water. Brine strength depends on the proportion of salt to water and no other ingredients are included in brine strength.

25. <u>Salometer</u> – a graduated hydrometer used for measuring the brine strength as percent salt in a brine solution. The salometer does this in relation to a saturated salt solution as follows: a 100° brine is saturated solution containing 26.4% salt. A 60° brine has .60% x 26.4% salt = 15.8 salt at 38°F (3.3°C).

26. <u>Pickle</u> – the completed solution ready for incorporation in to the meat product. It contains, in addition to salt, all other curing ingredients.

27. <u>Green weight</u> – the weight of the fresh, uncured, uncooked meat, before processing (bone-in, semiboneless or boneless).

28. <u>Percent pump</u> – the desired percentage increase in weight of primal cut above the green weight. For example, a 10% pump is 110 times the green weight. That is 10% pickle has been added to the raw meat.

29. <u>Cover Pickle</u> – a pickle that contains all ingredients at the same level as the pumping pickle except phosphate. Cured meats may be placed in cover pickle and refrigerated for several days to allow time for cure perfusion and equalization throughout product (used with small bone-in pieces, e.g., hocks, feet, neck bones).

30. <u>Cure</u> – sodium or potassium nitrite or nitrate is the cure. However, this term is used to define commercially blended cures which contain a specified amount of cure in addition to salt and/or coloring agents and buffers.

II. LAMB AND LAMB CARCASS EVALUATION

A. The following factors are used in evaluating live market lambs to estimate carcass characteristics, measure actual carcass characteristics, and calculate market value. These factors, with the exception of live weight, are determined by visual appraisal of the live animal. Stage of growth, genetic background, sex, and management history are all important in making useful estimates. Your estimates will be compared with and scored against actual carcass measurements. Figure 1 is a form to use in estimating the quality and yield grade properties of four individual market lambs. The important estimates/actuals of determining live and carcass market value are as follows:

   1. Live Weight (LW)
   2. Dressing Percent (DP)
   3. Hot Carcass Weight (HCW)
   4. Fat Thickness (used in the conversion to yield grade)
   5. Lower rib or body wall thickness
   6. Ribeye Area (REA)
   7. Leg Conformation (Score)
   8. Quality Grade (QG)
   9. Yield Grade (YG)

B. Live Weight
   1. Weight at time of evaluation
   2. Reasonable Range 95-145 lbs
   3. Average 120 lbs

C. Dressing Percent (DP)
   1. The definition of DP is $\dfrac{\text{Hot Carcass Weight} \times 100}{\text{Live Weight (LW)}}$

   2. A reasonable range of 45-58% and an average of 53% are useful pieces of information.

   3. Many factors affect DP. Some other factors in addition to live weight affecting DP are:
      a. Amount of fill (loss of fill increases DP and vice versa)
      b. Shorn vs. unshorn (shorn will have a higher DP than unshorn)
      c. Fatness (the fatter the lamb the higher the DP)

4.   On the basis of live weight, dressing percentage can be estimated as follows:

Live Weight	DP
80	48-49
90	50-51
100	52-53
110	54-55
120	56+

5.   DP is used to estimate hot carcass weight (HCW); calculated by DP x LW times live weight (LW)

D.   Fat Thickness

     1.   Estimation of fat thickness

         a.   Observation of the conformation of the live animal provides estimation of fatness. Those animals with angular conformation will be lean (0.10-.25 inch fat), and those animals with wide backs and full (deep) flanks will be fat as a general rule (0.3-.4 inch fat) over the center of the ribeye at the 12-13th rib interface.

         b.   Handling the lamb over the top of the back or over the ribs can be useful in estimating fat thickness; however, visual observation can be just as useful. Feeling bone over the back and ribs indicates leanness (0.10-.15) and feeling little or no bone means a fat lamb.

     2.   Measured between the 12th-13th ribs over the center of ribeye.

         a.   Possible range .05-0.6 inches

         b.   Average 0.20 inch

E.   Body wall or lower rib thickness is the total thickness of the body wall (fat, lean, and bone). This measurement is made 5 inches from midline curvilinear to the back at the 12th and 13th rib interface. Body wall thickness will be used in calculating percentage boneless, closely trimmed retail yield.

F.   Ribeye Area (REA)

     1.   An average 120 lb. lamb will have about a 2.4 square inch REA.

2. An estimation of REA, live, and carcass weight for average muscled lambs is as follows:

Live Wt (lb)	Carcass wt (lb)	REA (Sq. in)
75	40	1.9
95	50	2.2
115	60	2.4
130	72	2.6

3. Adjust REA according to muscling expressed in leg conformation. An average choice leg muscling score (11) is considered average conformation. To estimate live lamb leg conformation score, you need to visualize the dimensions of the leg as a carcass on the rail suspended from the hind legs.

    a. To a muscular lamb (thick, full leg) add 0.3 to 0.4 sq. in. Rams will be more muscular than wethers and wethers more muscular than ewes.

    b. To a poorly muscled lamb (one lacking thickness of leg and back) subtract 0.2 to 0.3 sq. in.

Figure 1.

ANIMAL SCIENCE LABORATORY
LAMB EVALUATION

	1	2	3	4
<u>Live Weight</u> (Given)	_____	_____	_____	_____
<u>Dressing Percent (DP)</u> (Range 45-58%, Ave 53%)	_____	_____	_____	_____
<u>Hot Carcass Weight (HCW)</u> (Live weight x dressing % (decimal)	_____	_____	_____	_____
<u>Adjusted Fat Thickness (AFT)</u> (12th—13th rib) over Ribeye Range 0.005-0.6 in. Ave = 0.20 in. for 120 lb. live lamb (Yield Grade (YG) use equation below)	AFT/YG ___ / ___	AFT/YG ___ / ___	AFT/YG ___ / ___	AFT/YG ___ / ___
<u>Ribeye Area</u> (12th & 13th rib) (Range of 1.5-4.0 in^2) (Ave. = 2.4 in^2 for 120 lb. live lamb)	_____	_____	_____	_____
<u>Leg Conformation Score</u> (Range 9-15, Ave. 11)	_____	_____	_____	_____
<u>Quality Grade (QG)</u> (Range Gd^+-Pr^+; Ave = Ch^+) <u>Carcass Value/cwt</u> (Base carcass price/cwt + or - YG price adjustment)	_____	_____	_____	_____
<u>Live Value/cwt</u> (Carcass Value/cwt x Standard Dressing %) (Standard Dressing % = 53%)	_____	_____	_____	_____

Yield Grade (YG) Equation $\qquad$ YG = 0.4 + (10 x adjusted fat thickness)

<u>Leg Score</u> 9 (Gd^+);10 (Ch^-); 11 ($Ch°$); 12 (Ch^+); 13 (Pr^-);14 ($Pr°$); 15 (Pr^+)

4.   Lamb carcasses are seldom ribbed commercially. In judging and carcass contests, and instructional classes, they will be ribbed by cutting across the ribeye (*longissimus thoracis*) between the 12th and 13th rib. Ribeye is not a part of official lamb carcass yield grade standards, but its estimation will give some information about muscling and is used in calculating percentage boneless, closely trimmed retail yield. The ribeye is measured in square inches by using a plastic grid calibrated to 0.05 in^2.

G. Determination of USDA Lamb Carcass Yield Grades

1.   The yield of a market lamb or lamb carcass is determined exclusively by evaluating/measuring the amount of external fat. Formerly leg muscling score and kidney and pelvic fat were components of yield grades. As the amount of external fat increases, the percentage of retail cuts decreases and the numerical yield grade increases. The yield grade numbers used by industry are 1, 2, 3, 4 and 5. In class, yield grades will be estimated to the nearest 0.1 of a YG. Also, in class, each actual yield grade number will be determined to the nearest 0.1 of a YG using the USDA yield grade equation, i.e., YG = 0.4 + (10 x adjusted fat thickness). Also, see Table 3 for conversion of fat thickness to yield grade.

2.   Fat thickness is a single measurement made over the center of the ribeye (Longissimus thoracis) muscle perpendicular to the outside surface between the 12th and 13th ribs. These measurements may include adjustments, as appropriate, to reflect unusual amounts of fat, or lack thereof, on other parts of the carcass.

3.   USDA yield grade determination

a. Determine fat thickness over the center of the ribeye between the 12th and 13th ribs. It is not unusual to adjust yield grade accordingly to reflect unusual amounts of fat deposition, or lack thereof, on other parts of the animal/carcass. The USDA lamb carcass standards for yield grades based on fat thickness over the center of the ribeye are as follows:

Yield grade 1 – 0.00 - 0.15 inch of fat

    Yield grade 2 - 0.16 - 0.25 inch of fat

    Yield grade 3 - 0.26 - 0.35 inch of fat

    Yield grade 4 - 0.36 - 0.45 inch of fat

    Yield grade 5 - >0.46 inch of fat

Conversion of these fat thicknesses to yield grade are based on the following USDA yield grade equation:

Yield Grade = 0.4 + (10 x adjusted fat thickness)

    b.   Clues for visual estimation/evaluation of fatness

        1)   Overall fatness can be determined best by determining the anatomical sites of rapid fat deposition over the leg, sirloin, loin, rack, shoulder, breast, flank edge and cod/udder. Rams will usually be leaner (less fat) than wethers and wethers will have less fat than ewes.

        2)   The shape or conformation of the animal/carcass provides a basis for estimating fatness. Muscular animals/carcasses will be more angular in their conformation because of smaller amounts of fat on the body, whereas fat animals will be wider (thicker) over the back, especially over the sirloin/leg, the back will be fuller and rounder, bodies will appear deeper than muscular animals, and the animal will have a narrower base.

    c.   Kidney and pelvic fat (KP) must be removed in the slaughter area. To be eligible for USDA grading, lamb carcasses cannot have more than 1.0 percent of their carcass weight as KF fat. Therefore there is no adjustment of YG for KP.

H. Determination of USDA Lamb Carcass Quality Grade

    1.   To determine the quality grade of a lamb carcass separate evaluation of two general characteristics is required. First, the quality or the palatability (tenderness, juiciness, flavor) indicating characteristics of the lean is estimated by determining the degree (amount) of fat streaking, brightness of flank muscle color, firmness of the flank, and bone maturity (color and shape of rib bones, and presence of break joints). Secondly, the conformation of the carcass is estimated by observing the thickness of muscling, especially leg muscling and proportion of muscle to skeletal makeup. Consequently, the final quality grade is made using equal compensations for fat streaking and leg conformation within the limitations of each quality grade at a particular maturity.

        The quality grades of lambs are Prime, Choice, Good and Utility. Most market lambs (90%) will grade Choice. That is, they will have slight and small amounts (degrees) of fat streaking in their flanks dependent on their maturities. Muscular conformation will equally compensate for flank streaking. However, regardless of Prime conformation, a lamb must have flank streaking equivalent to Prime before it can grade Prime. A few lambs will grade Prime such as ewes or more mature wethers because of greater fat deposition in the flank lean.

a. The quality of the lean is evaluated by observing the quantity of fat streakings within and upon the inside flank muscles in relation to the apparent evidence of maturity. In addition, a minimum degree of firmness of lean flesh and external fat for each grade and a minimum degree of external fatness for carcasses would characterize Prime and Choice grades. In evaluating market lambs, body composition (fatness) and sex of the lamb are two good potential indicators of quality grade. For example, ewes will usually be fatter than wethers and are expected to have a greater degree of flank streaking. Wethers are usually fatter than rams and would be expected to have a higher degree of flank streaking than rams.

b. Conformation counts equally as much as flank streaking in lamb carcass quality grading. The conformation descriptions for each grade specification refer to the thickness of muscling and to an overall degree of thickness and fullness of the carcass. For example, as described in USDA Standards, lamb carcasses having minimum conformation qualifications for the Prime grade (see Figure 2 for average Prime leg score conformation, 14) tend to be thickly muscled throughout, are moderately wide and thick in relation to their length, have moderately plump and full legs, moderately wide and thick backs, and moderately thick and full shoulders. Regardless of the extent to which the conformation of a carcass may exceed the minimum requirements for Prime, a carcass must have minimum Prime quality, primarily degree of flank streaking at that particular maturity to be eligible for the Prime grade. Figure 3 is an example of a lamb carcass having an average Choice leg score (11). There is a numerical scoring system equivalent (the higher the number, the more muscular) to one third of a leg muscling as follows:

Leg Score
9 Good[+]
10 Choice[-]
11 Choice[°]
12 Choice[+]
13 Prime[-]
14 Prime[°]
15 Prime[+]

Figure 1. Example of an average choice leg conformation.

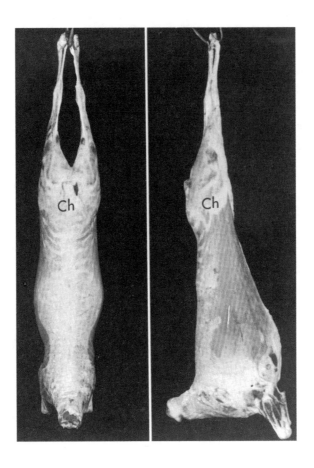

Figure 2. Example of an average prime leg conformation.

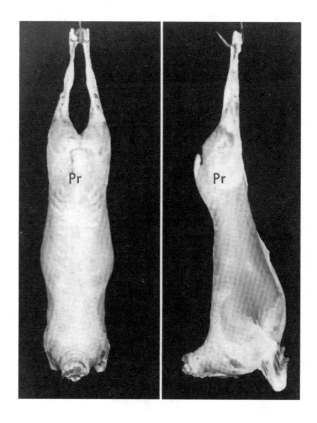

c. Maturity is the subjective appraisal of the physiological maturity based on the presence or absence of break joints (see Figure 9), lean color of flank, shape and color of rib bones, and flank firmness. These indicators of physiological maturity are assessed for the purpose of determining chronological age and correlating flank fat streaking to QG. Consequently, correct evaluation of maturity is an important part of quality grades, and is used as a significant factor to determine quality grade and market value.

Figure 4. Examples of break and spool joints in the forelimb of lamb carcasses.

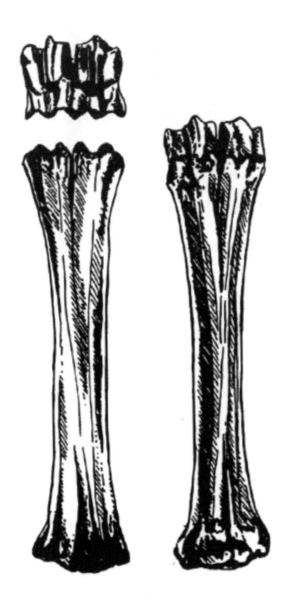

2).   There are three kinds of market lambs.

        a.   Young lamb (4-12 months) Lamb carcasses have the presence of at least one break joint. The physiological characteristics of lamb carcasses of A maturity correspond to 4-6 month old lambs. A+ to B- maturity corresponds to 6-9 months, and B maturity corresponds to 9-12 month old lambs.

        b.   Yearling mutton (12-24 months) has the presence of two spool joints.

        c.   Mutton (24 months and older) has two spool joints and more mature carcass properties than yearling mutton.

Table 1.   Maturity descriptions of three classes of young lamb carcasses based on rib bone color and shape and flank muscle color are as follows:

Factors	A maturity 4-6 months	A+ to B- maturity 6-9 months	B maturity 9-12 months
Break joint color	Very red	Slightly red	White
Rib bone color	Red	Slightly red	White
Rib bone shape	Round	Slightly round	Flat
Flank lean color	Bright pinkish red	Pinkish red	Dark Red

2.   After making your estimate for stage of maturity, degree of flank streaking and conformation, you should now refer to Figure 9 to determine lamb carcass quality grade. The amount of flank streaking at that particular maturity gives the preliminary quality grade. Degrees of flank fat streaking must increase as maturity increases to qualify for a similar preliminary quality grade. For final quality grade, leg muscling score is equivalent to flank streaking. Consequently, adjustment for leg muscling can cause an adjustment upward or downward for overall quality grade.

For example, a mid point small degree of flank streaking for mid point maturity young lamb (A^{50}) would preliminarily have qualifications for low prime. The lamb has a high prime leg score (15), and therefore would have a final quality grade of average prime.

        a.   When officially graded, slaughter lamb carcasses must be identified for both quality and yield grades, i.e., they must have quality and yield grade marks.

Figure 5.

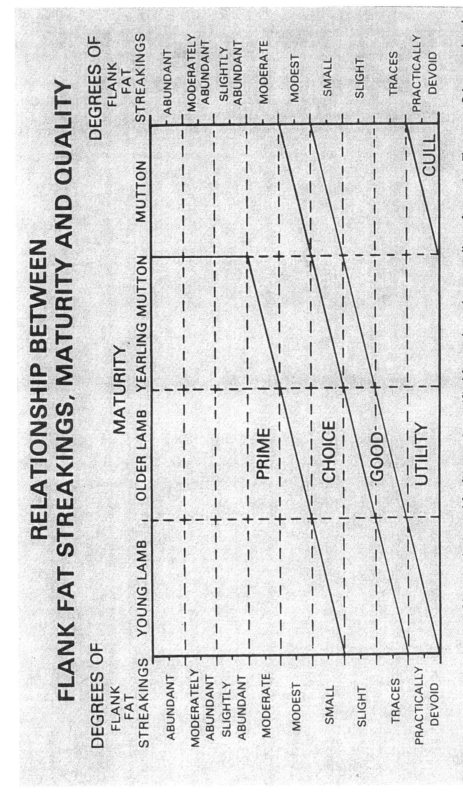

I.   Percentage boneless, closely trimmed retail yield (%BCTRY) base factors and adjustments

Base Factors	Adjustment
% BCTRY = 47%	
Hot carcass weight = 60 lbs	$\pm$ 10 lb = $\pm$ .85%
Fat thickness = .2 inch	$\pm$ 0.1 inch = $\pm$ .44%
Body wall thickness = .8 inch	$\pm$ 0.1 inch = $\pm$ .35%
Rib eye area = 2.4 inch^2	$\pm$ 0.1 inch = $\pm$ .25%

Example

Live weight 120 lb

DP 55%

Hot carcass weight, 66 lb	- .50
(Subtract because heavier than 60 lbs)	
Fat thickness, 0.2 inch	0
Body wall, 1.0 inch	- .70
(Subtract because more than 0.8 inch)	
Rib eye area, 2.6 inch^2	+ .50
(Add because more than 2.4 inch^2)	_____
	- .70

Base % BCTRY $\pm$ (adjustment) = % BCTRY

47.0 + (-.70) = 46.30%   BCTRY

III. SWINE AND PORK CARCASS EVALUATION

A.   The following factors are used in evaluating live market hogs to estimate carcass characteristics, to measure actual carcass characteristics, and calculate market value. These factors, with the exception of live weight, are determined by visual appraisal of the live animal. Stage of growth, genetic background, sex, and management history are important in making useful estimates. The significant estimates/actual of determining live and carcass market value are as follows:

1. Live Weight (LW)
2. Dressing Percent (DP)
3. Hot Carcass Weight (HCW) used to calculate lbs. of fat-free lean and percent fat-free lean
4. Last Rib Backfat used in calculating USDA Grade
5. Fat Depth over Loin Eye (10th rib fat) used in calculating percent fat-free lean
6. 10th Rib Loin Eye (Muscle) area used in calculating fat-free lean
7. Ham Muscling Score used in calculating USDA Grade
8. Length (See Figure 7)
9. Percent Fat-Free Lean
10. USDA Grade

B.   Dressing Percent (DP):

1. $$DP = \frac{\text{Hot Carcass Weight}}{\text{Live Weight}} \times 100$$

2. A reasonable range for barrows and gilts is 68-78%. Barrows will have slightly greater DP than gilts, as barrows are usually fatter than gilts. A reasonable average is 73%.

3.Several factors affect DP in swine. Two major ones are:

    a. Amount of fat and muscle – the fatter and the more muscular the animal, the greater the DP

    b. Amount of fill (intestinal and stomach contents) The greater the fill the lower the DP and vice versa.

4. It is used in determining hot carcass weight and then for calculating percentage fat-free muscle.

Figure 6.   ANIMAL SCIENCE LABORATORY
SWINE EVALUATION

	1	2	3	4
<u>Live Weight</u> (Given)	_____	_____	_____	_____
<u>Dressing Percent (DP)</u> (70-78%) Ave. = 73%	_____	_____	_____	_____
<u>Hot Carcass Weight</u> (HCW) (Live Weight x Dressing %)	_____	_____	_____	_____
<u>Fat Depth Over Loin Eye</u> ($10^{th} - 11^{th}$ Rib) (Normal range 0.4-1.1 in)	_____	_____	_____	_____
<u>Loin Eye Area</u> (Normal Range 6.0-9.0 in^2) Ave. for 200 lb carcass	_____	_____	_____	_____
<u>NPPC % Lean</u> Pounds of Fat-Free Lean =				
a) 8.588 + 0.465 x HCW	_____	_____	_____	_____
b) -21.9 x 10th Rib Fat Depth	_____	_____	_____	_____
c) +3.005 x 10th Rib LEA	_____	_____	_____	_____
<u>Pounds of Fat-Free Lean</u> {Sum of Values (a+b+c)}	_____	_____	_____	_____
<u>Percent Fat-Free Lean</u> (Pounds of Muscle divided by HCW x 100)	_____	_____	_____	_____
<u>Carcass Value</u> (per cwt) (Base carcass price/cwt + or - % muscle price adj)	_____	_____	_____	_____
<u>Live Value</u> (per cwt) (Carcass Value x Standard Dressing %) (Standard DP = 73%)	_____	_____	_____	_____
<u>Last Rib Backfat</u> (Normal Range 0.3-1.1 in)Ave. = 0.7 in	_____	_____	_____	_____
<u>Ham Muscling Score</u> (1=Thin; 2=Ave.; 3=Thick)	_____	_____	_____	_____
<u>USDA Grade</u> (4 x Last Rib Backfat – Muscle Score)	_____	_____	_____	_____
<u>Color Score (1-6)</u>	_____	_____	_____	_____
<u>Firmness Score (1-5)</u>	_____	_____	_____	_____
<u>Marbling Score (1-6; 10)</u>	_____	_____	_____	_____

C. Fat thickness (depth) over the loin eye (10th rib fat)
   1. Fat over the loin eye or 10th rib fat thickness (depth)
      a. In estimating fat thickness over the loin eye, select the 10 -11th rib site, and at 3-4 inches lateral from the midline. A market hog showing angularity over the top, trim jowl, and flank will be lean (.8 inch or less of fat). Conversely, a market hog having a flat top, deep sides, fat jowl and full flanks will be fat (1.2 and greater).
      b. In a pork carcass, it is a single measurement, made at the 10th rib, three fourths of the
         length of the loin eye from the medial (bone) side.
      c. It is measured perpendicular to the skin surface and includes skin thickness.
      d. It is used in calculating fat-free lean.
      e. The average market hog has about 0.8 of fat depth over the loin eye.
   2. Last Rib Backfat Thickness (See Figure 7)
      a. Estimate fat at the last rib, midline of the back.
      b. It is taken opposite the last rib at the connective tissue-fat interface and includes the skin.
      c. It is used in determining USDA grade.
   c. The average market hog has about 0.8 inches of last rib backfat.

Table 2.

Relationship Between Last Rib and 10th Rib Fat Depth (in.)

Last Rib (in)	10th Rib (in)
.60	.45
.80	.80
1.00	1.20
1.20	1.50
1.40	1.90

   3. Average Backfat Thickness (See Figure 7)
      a. Historically, average backfat was the measurement used to evaluate fatness of market hogs—average of three backfat thickness measurements. Each is taken opposite the first rib, last rib, and last lumbar vertebra at the connective tissue-fat interface and to include the skin.
      b. A reasonable average backfat range is 0.6-1.2 inches with 0.9 inches of average backfat as a reasonable average. Average backfat is not used today.
   4. Actual measurements of fat thickness of carcasses are made with a ruler or, in commercial settings, with ultrasonics or fiber optic probes.

Figure 7.   Anatomical sites for measuring backfat (fat depth/thickness) and carcass length.

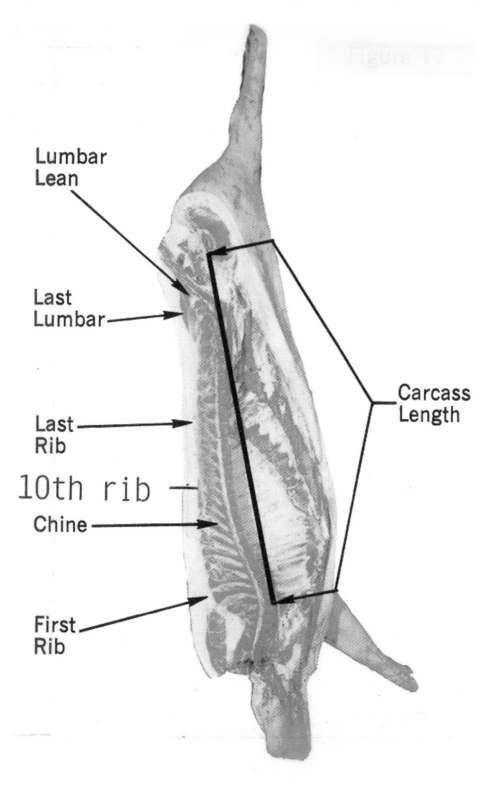

Lumbar Lean

Last Lumbar

Last Rib

10th rib

Chine

First Rib

Carcass Length

D.   Loin Eye Area (See Figure 8):

1.   The area of the longissimus muscle at the interface of the $10^{th} - 11^{th}$ ribs is measured usually by using a transparent plastic grid calibrated in 0.05 inches.
2.   A reasonable range 6.0-9.0 sq. in., average 7.5 sq. in.
3.   used in determining percent fat free lean.
4.   Guidelines for estimating loin eye muscle based on live weight and muscularity are as follows:

      a.   <u>Average Muscled Hogs</u>

Live Wt (lb)	LEA (in^2)
200	6.0
220	6.7
240	7.2
260	7.7
280	8.2

      b.   <u>260 lb Live Market Hog</u>

Muscle Type	LEA (in^2)
Poor	5.0
Average	7.0
Very Good	8.0
Excellent	9.0

Figure 8.   Sites for measuring fat depth (thickness) including skin at the 10th rib interface and loin eye area (dashed lines).

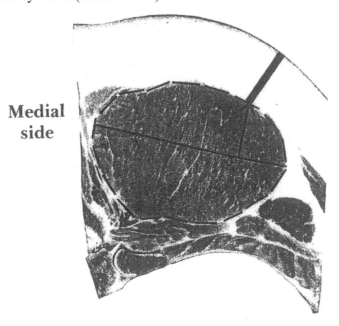

Medial side

E. Percent Fat-Free Lean
1. Definition: [weight (lbs) of total fat-free muscle in the carcass, divided by hot carcass weight x 100]. A reasonable range would be 42-62%; the average market hog would have about 55% muscle.
2. Percent muscle is used to determine market value.
3. The three factors used in determining percent muscle are
   a. Fat thickness (depth) at the 10th rib to include skin [over the loin eye three quarters the length of the eye from the medial (bone) side].
   b. Loin eye area at the 10th-11th rib interface
   c. Hot carcass weight as calculated from estimated DP times market weight
4. The method for determining lbs of fat-free lean is as follows:
   a. Pounds of Fat Free Lean =
      8.59 + (0.465 x HCW) – 21.90 x 10th Rib Fat Depth (in.) + 3.00 x LEA at tenth rib (in^2).
   b. Percent fat free lean is calculated by (pounds of fat free lean ÷ hot carcass weight) x 100

F. USDA Pork Carcass Grading System
1. No pork carcasses are graded by USDA graders in commercial plants today. However, the system includes features that are applied in many different systems designed to predict pork carcass composition. For example the USDA system applies a carcass fat estimate (last rib fat) and an estimate of muscle (muscle score). Grades for barrows and gilts are based on two general considerations: little emphasis on quality and heavy emphasis on expected yield of lean cuts. Quality is either acceptable or unacceptable and refers to the characteristics of both the lean and fat of a carcass. Few pork carcasses are ribbed commercially, which makes it difficult to assess marbling and color of lean. However, ribbed pork carcasses can be readily scored for degree of marbling, lean color, (see Figure 9) and firmness (see Figure 10). In the USDA standards, however, the expected yield of four lean cuts from each of the four grades is predicted on the basis of last rib backfat and ham muscling score. Consequently, pork carcass grades based on last rib fat thickness and ham muscling, give some indication of yield of four lean cuts.

2. | Grades | USDA Yields (Chilled Carcass Basis) |
    | --- | --- |
    | a. No. 1 | 60.4% and over |
    | b. No. 2 | 57.4-60.3% |
    | c. No. 3 | 54.4-57.3% |
    | d. No. 4 | Less than 54.4% |
    | e. Utility – | Inferior quality of lean, soft oily fat, and thin belly |

3. Factors for determining USDA grade
   a. Last rib backfat thickness
   b. Ham muscling score
4. Preliminary grade based on backfat thickness over the last rib

Preliminary grade	Backfat thickness range
U.S. No. 1	Less than 1.00 inch
U.S. No. 2	1.00 to 1.24 inch
U.S. No. 3	1.25 to 1.49 inch
U.S. No. 4	1.50 inches and over

5. Three ham muscling scores (see Figure 10) are used to estimate carcass muscling
   a. Thin (TN) (inferior) (1) angular and thin
   b. Intermediate or Average (2)
   c. Thick (TK) (superior) (3)
6. Grade adjustment is based on amount of ham muscling
   a. Barrow and gilt carcasses with average muscling will be graded according to their last rib backfat thickness range. For a carcass to grade US No. 1 it must have at least intermediate or average muscling
   b. Carcasses with thin muscling will be graded one grade lower than indicated by last rib backfat thickness range (i.e., prelims at U.S. No. 1 would be a US No. 2).
   c. Carcasses with thick muscling will be graded one grade higher than indicated by their last rib backfat thickness (i.e., prelims at U.S. No. 2 would be a US No. 1, range except that carcasses with 1.75 inches or greater last rib backfat thickness must remain a U.S. No. 4 grade).
7. Grade determination of a barrow or gilt carcass with acceptable lean quality and belly thickness is as follows:
   a. Carcass Grade = (4 x last rib backfat thickness, inches) (1.0 x muscling score)
   b. To apply this equation, muscling should be scored as follows: thin muscling = 1, intermediate or average muscling = 2, and thick muscling = 3
   c. Examples:
   1) Last rib backfat = 1.0; Muscling score = (intermediate) (2)
      $(4 \times 1.0) - (1.0 \times 2) = 4 - 2 = 2.0$
      2) Last rib backfat = 1.15; Muscling score = thick (3)
         $(4 \times 1.15) - (1.0 \times 3) = 4.6 - 3 = 1.6$

Figure 9.   Pork Marbling and Color Scores

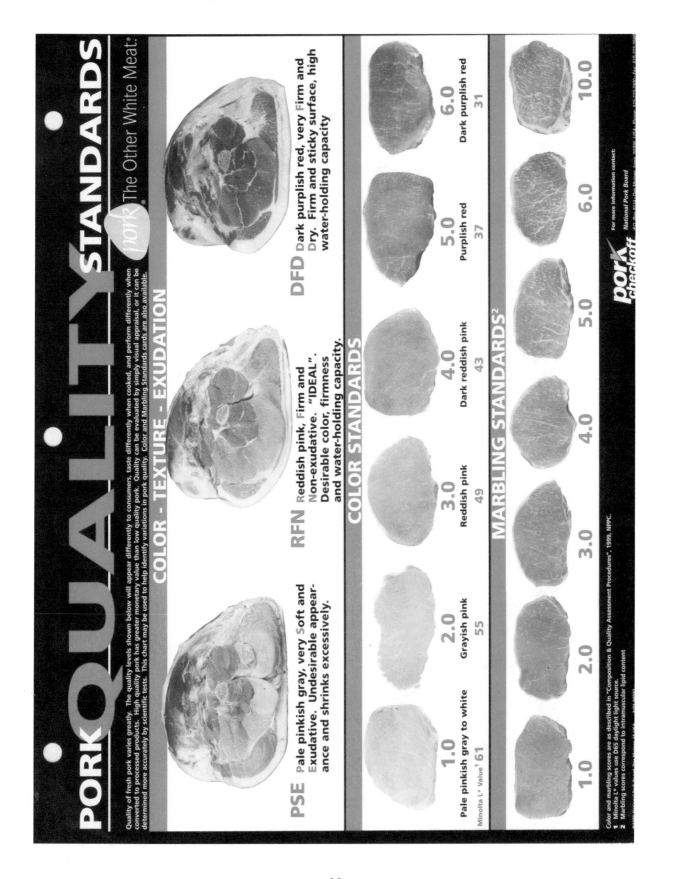

Figure 10.   Firmness/Wetness Scores

1*
Very Soft
and Very Watery

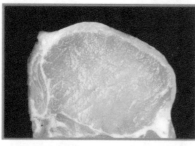

2*
Soft
and Watery

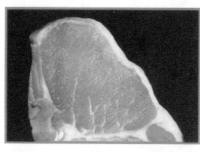

3
Slightly Firm
and Moist

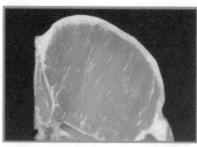

4
Firm and
Moderately Dry

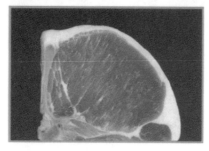

5
Very Firm
and Dry

Figure 11.   Pork Carcass (Ham) Muscling Scores.

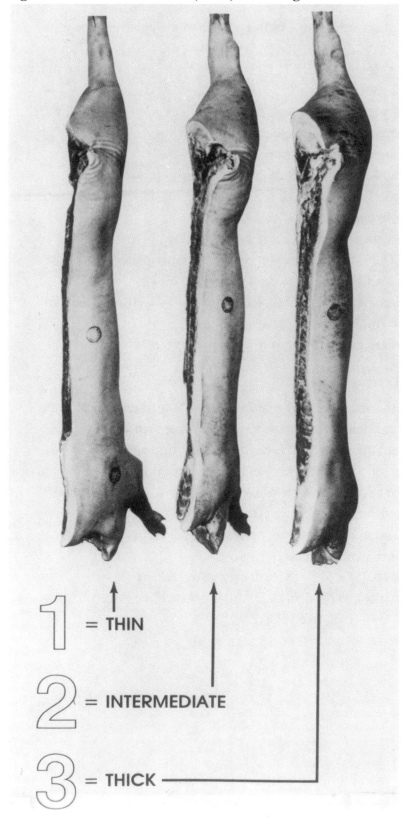

G. Length (See Figure 7):
    1.   It is measured from the anterior edge of the first rib to the anterior edge of the aitch bone.
    2.   A reasonable range in length is 28 - 34 inches and a typical market hog will have an average of 31.0 inches.

H. The systematic process of calculating carcass and live hog market prices is as follows:
    1.   Estimate dressing percent (DP) for calculating hot carcass weight (live weight x DP as a decimal = hog carcass weight)
    2.   Estimate percent muscle on a hot carcass weight basis as follows:
        a.   Estimate hot carcass weight, loin eye area (or loin muscle area-LMA) and fat depth over the loin eye.
        b.   If the carcass has been skinned, divide hot weight by .94 to adjust back to a skin-on basis. (The skin component represents approximately 6% of the carcass)
        c.   Pounds of Fat Free Lean = 8.59 + (0.465 x HCW) – (21.90 x 10th Rib Fat Depth) + (3.00 x 10th Rib LEA)
        d.   Percent Fat-Free Lean = $\dfrac{\text{Pounds of Fat-Free Lean} \times 100}{\text{HCW}}$

3. Example and calculations of carcass and live value per cwt.
        a.   Assume for this example only that for every 1% difference between estimated/actual and base carcass percent fat-free lean, $0.75 would be added to or subtracted from the current carcass price per cwt. If the current price for pork carcasses yielding 50 percent fat-free lean (base) is $55 per cwt, and your estimate of the live hog is 52.4% muscle and 74 DP, then estimated carcass price per cwt =
        b.   Estimated percent muscle – base percent muscle x price differential + price per cwt = carcass value/cwt
               (52.4 – 50.0) (0.75) + $55 = $56.80 carcass value/cwt
        c.   Carcass price per cwt ($56.80) x DP (.74) per cwt live price
               $56.80 x 0.74 = $42.00 live value/cwt

IV. BEEF CATTLE AND BEEF CARCASS EVALUATION

A. The following factors are used in evaluating live market beef to estimate carcass characteristics, measure actual carcass characteristics, and calculate market value. These factors, with the exception of live weight, are determined by visual appraisal of the live animal. The stage of growth, genetic background, sex, and management history are important in making useful estimates. Beef carcass grading defines value but is also used for branding of products. Therefore accurate classification within quality and grade groups is very critical. We will use visual grading approaches in our laboratory, but instrument grading has become very common. Camera based grading systems are capable of assigning beef yield grades to the 0.1 of a yield grade and quality grades to specific ranges. Features of beef cattle evaluation and beef carcass evaluation include:

1. **Live Weight (LW)**

2. **Dressing Percent (DP)**

3. **Hot Carcass Weight (HCW)**

4. **Fat Thickness (FT) used in determining preliminary yield (PYG)**

5. **Ribeye Area (REA) used in calculating beef YG**

6. **Kidney, Pelvic and Heart Fat (KPH) used in calculating beef YG**

7. **Yield Grade (YG) YG = PYG + (± adjustments for REA and KPH)**

8. **Quality Grade (QG)**

B. Live Weight

Live weight is the actual weight usually determined at the farm or at time of market. Live weight (LW) is used to calculate hot carcass weight (HCW), (i.e., estimated DP x LW = HWC). HCW is necessary for making estimates and adjustments for REA and KPH. Range in live weight is 900 to 1500 pounds. Average live weight is about 1150 pounds.

C. Dressing Percent (DP)

1. DP defined <u>Hot Carcass Weight (HCW)</u> X 100

   Live Weight

2. Reasonable Range 55–65% for steers, heifers, and bullocks with an average DP of 62% for Choice medium-framed beef steers and heifers; bullocks lower. Usually, heifers and steers are fatter than bullocks (young bulls). Consequently, as a rule of thumb, they will have higher DP than bullocks. Cows have wider variation and usually lower DP (50-58%) than steers, heifers, and bullocks.

3. Estimating dressing percentage (DP) is a challenging exercise because so many factors can affect it. It is still used in marketing livestock even with all of its shortcomings. One reasonable way of estimating DP for medium-framed steers and heifers is live weight. Estimation of DP is most important in calculating a carcass weight for ribeye area estimation. The following LW/DP data give a "ball park" figure for estimating DP. After estimating a DP for the live animal, multiply it times live weight to obtain a hot carcass weight. Hot carcass weight is needed for estimating ribeye area. Use the data in Table 3 for hot carcass weight-ribeye area relationship to determine the required REA for that particular weight. The average hot carcass weight of a market steer today is about 750 lbs. One way of estimating dressing percentage based on live weight is as follows:

Live Wt (LW)	DP
800	58
900	60
1000	62
1100	63
1200	64
1300	65

Figure 12. Beef Cattle Evaluation and Carcass Estimation Worksheet

	1	2	3	4
Live Weight (Given)				
Dressing Percent (DP) (Range 58–65%, Ave 62%)				
Hot Carcass Weight (HCW) (Live Weight x Dressing % as a decimal)				
Fat Thickness over Ribeye (12–13th rib) Range of .1–1.0 in. Ave. = .45 in. for 1150 lb live animal (See conversion chart of FT to PYG below)	FT PYG	FT PYG	FT PYG	FT PYG
Ribeye Area (REA) (12th & 13th rib) 9–16 in.^{2} average 12.5 in.^{2} for a 725 lb carcass) Adjust ± .30 PYG for each 1 in.^{2} to or from required REA	ADJ	ADJ	ADJ	ADJ
% Kidney Pelvic and Heart Fat (% KPH) Range 1.0–5.5% Ave. 2.5% Adjust ± .20 PYG to or from 3.5% for each ± 1% KPH	ADJ	ADJ	ADJ	ADJ
Yield Grade (YG) (Range 1–5.9) (PYG ± adj factors for ribeye area and KPH = YG) Ave = 3.1				
Quality Grade (QG) (Young beef, range=standard to high prime; old, C bone or older, range = low Utility to high Commercial				
Carcass Value/cwt (Base carcass price/cwt ± YG price adjustment)				
Live Value/cwt (Carcass Value/cwt x Standard Dressing % as a decimal) (Standard Dressing % = 62%)				

Conversion of FT to PYG		% KPH FAT ADJUSTMENTS	CARCASS WEIGHT- REA RELATIONSHIP	
FAT THICKNESS (FT) OVER 12TH–13TH RIB	PRELIMINARY YIELD GRADE (PYG)		WEIGHT	REA
.20 inch =	2.50	1.0% = -.50	500	9.8
.30 =	2.75	1.5% = -.40	600	11.0
.40 =	3.00	2.0% = -.30	650	11.6
.50 =	3.25	2.5% = -.20	700	12.2
.60 =	3.50	3.0% = -.10	750	12.8
.80 =	4.00	3.5% = -0.0	800	13.4
1.0 =	4.50	4.5% = +.20	850	14.0

4. Factors affecting DP

    a. Amount of fill (stomach and intestinal content) – greater the fill the lower DP and vice versa

    b. Amount of fatness and muscling – greater fatness and muscling result in a higher DP

    c. Weight of hide – heavier the hide the lower the DP

    d. Pregnancy – lowers DP

5. DP is used to estimate hot carcass weight (HCW) by multiplying it times live weight (LW).

D. Fat Thickness

1. Clues for making reasonable visual estimates of fat thickness

    a. Estimation of fat is the first and most important estimate an evaluator can make because fat accounts for about two-thirds of the variation in yield grade. After estimating fat thickness, it is converted to a preliminary yield grade (PYG). The greater the fat thickness, the higher the preliminary yield grade number and vice versa. Preliminary yield grade is inversely proportional to cutability (percentage of retail product). That is, a low number (e.g., PYG 2.0) indicates a high cutability whereas a high number (e.g., PYG 4.0) means a low cutability.

    b. Astute visual appraisal of conformation can help determine fatness/leanness. Live animals that have wide backs that are flat over the top and deep sided and have full brisket, flank, and cod/udder are fat (i.e., 0.8–1.2 inches of fat over the eye). Conversely, angularity of back and top and trim brisket, flank, and cod/udder are indices of trimness (i.e., 0.15–.3 inches of fat thickness).

    c. Handling (feeling with the hands to estimate fat cover over the backbone and ribs) gives some evidence of fatness/leanness. When one feels bone, this usually means little fat (e.g., 0.15 inches of fat over the ribeye) whereas if no bone is felt, there is fat (e.g., 0.6 – 0.8 inches of fat over the ribeye). Visual observation, however, can be just as useful for obtaining evaluation data and is certainly safer.

    d. Heifers are usually fatter than steers, and heifers and steers are usually fatter than bullocks. A wide variation in fatness can occur in cows depending on nutritional regime and productivity cycle.

2. A reasonable range is 0.1 to 1.0 inches, and a mean of about 0.45 inches for steers and heifers at 12th and 13th rib.

3.   On the live animal, it is subjectively estimated between the 12th and 13th ribs and three fourths laterally from the midline. In a carcass, it is measured 3/4 length of the ribeye from the split chine-bone site at the 12th rib (see Figure 12) opposite the ribeye. A steel ruler calibrated in 0.1 inch at one end and preliminary yield grades at the other end is used to make this measurement.

E.   Ribeye area (REA) estimation (see Figure 13). The first step is to estimate DP to obtain a hot carcass weight. Then check the hot carcass weight–ribeye area relationship in Table 3. Select the ribeye area for that particular hot carcass weight and then make an adjustment for muscularity.

1.   Ribeye area is a measure of muscling and is the muscling factor used to determine yield grade. The more muscular (larger the ribeye) the carcass the lower the yield grade number and vice versa.

2.   A reasonable range for REA is 9–16 square inches A 1000 lb steer with a 62% DP would have a hot carcass weight of 620 lb, corresponding to an 11.3 in^2 ribeye. The average steer today should have a 12.8 in^2 ribeye (750 lb hot carcass weight). Using 13.8 in^2 as an example, there would be an adjustment of -0.3 of a YG (1 in^2 = .3 YG), and subtract because of being more muscular resulting in a lower yield grade number and a higher cutability. On the other hand, an 11.8 in^2 would result in a +0.3 YG adjustment because of not being as muscular as it should be at that hot carcass weight. You will note for each 25 lb increase in hot carcass weight, ribeye area must increase 0.3 in^2. Extrapolation can be made for each 8 lbs of hot carcass weight.

3.   One way of estimating ribeye area based on live and carcass weights is as follows:

Live Wt.	Hot Carcass Wt.	REA
850	500	9.8
960	600	11.0
1100	700	12.2
1250	800	13.4

4. Adjust accordingly for muscularity, or lack of muscularity, as evidenced by thickness of round, shoulder, and width between front and back legs. For a lighter muscled beef animal than the average, reduce the ribeye area by 1 – 2 square inches. Conversely, for heavier muscled beef animals than the average, add 1 to 3 square inches. Bullocks will have larger ribeyes than steers and steers will have slightly larger ribeyes than heifers.

5. REA is actually measured on carcasses at the 12–13th rib interface (longissimus thoracis) (see Figure 12) by usually using a plastic grid calibrated in 0.1 square inches.

Figure 13.   Site for determining fat thickness (steel ruler) and ribeye area (dark) of the ribeye muscle (plastic grid) of a beef carcass at the 12–13th rib interface.

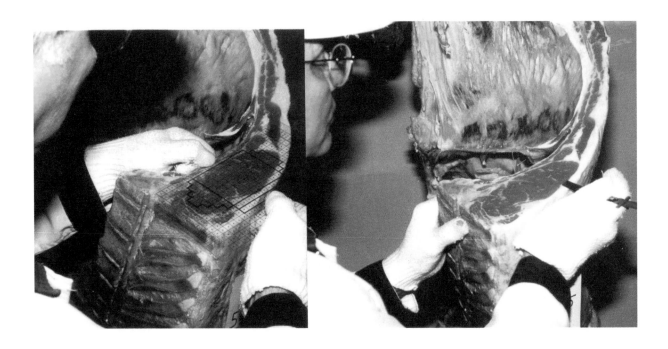

Table 3. Carcass Weight – Area of Ribeye Relationship

Warm Carcass Weight (lbs)	Area of Ribeye (sq. in.)
500	9.8
525	10.1
550	10.4
575	10.7
600	11.0
625	11.3
650	11.6
675	11.9
700	12.2
725	12.5
750	12.8
775	13.1
800	13.4
825	13.7
850	14.0
875	14.3
900	14.6
925	14.9
950	15.2
975	15.5

F.   Kidney, Pelvic and Heart Fat (KPH)

1.   A KPH of 3.5% is considered typical in the present USDA YG standards. That is, 3.5 percent of the carcass weight is kidney, pelvic and heart fat and, therefore, no adjustment in YG is made when a carcass has 3.5% KPH. KPH is a measure of internal fats and, therefore, is a factor used in yield grading. The higher the percentage of KPH the higher the yield grade number and the lower the cutability.

2.   Although estimation of percent KPH on the basis of fat thickness of the live animal is sometimes used, it is not at all satisfactory or recommended for estimating percent KPH

of today's beef cattle. Most market beef will have 2.0–2.5% KPH. This would be an adjustment of -.3 to -.2 of a YG (i.e., for each 1% from the base of 3.5% KPH an adjustment of +.2 YG would occur). Normally in crossbred cattle, an adjustment of -.2 or -.3 of a YG would be appropriate. In very lean cattle, as little as 1% KPH can be found (an adjustment of -.5 YG). Whereas, in very fat cattle (e.g., 1.0 inch of fat over the ribeye), an adjustment of +.1 to +.2 YG can occur (4–4.5% KPH, respectively). Although KPH includes heart fat, percentage KPH is primarily the weight of the kidney knob and pelvic fat (with 0.5 inch of fat cover remaining over the tenderloin) to the hot weight of the carcass. (lbs KPH/HCW) x 100 = % KPH).

G. Determination of Beef Quality Grades. Estimation of quality grades of live animals is based on the knowledge that 90 percent of our young beef (A and B maturities) grade Select or low Choice. The quality grades as used commercially for young beef are Prime, Choice, Select and Standard. Most commonly, grades are assigned to a 1/3 to 1/2 of a grade (i.e., low and high Select; low, average and high Choice). Specific grade assignments are critical as they are the basis for specifications for "Brands" such as Certified Angus Beef.

Some young beef cattle deposit abundant degrees of marbling and, therefore, will qualify for Prime quality grades. Heifers, because they mature earlier than steers, will deposit intramuscular fat (marbling) earlier, and consequently, grade higher than steers. Bullocks will usually have less intramuscular fat than steers and will grade lower. Actual quality grading of beef carcasses is determined principally on the basis of two factors: maturity and marbling. Maturity of the live animal is assessed visually or known birthdate; whereas, maturity of a carcass is done by subjectively assessing the physiological maturity of the bone in the vertebral column and rib bones, and lean color. Evaluating the degree of marbling in the exposed ribeye between the 12th and 13th ribs is determined by visual analysis. Camera grading systems are now in place in many commercial plants. Once a USDA grader has determined these criteria, a quality grade is placed on the carcass. Quality grade refers to the palatability indicating characteristics of the lean.

1. Maturity of a carcass is determined by visually observing the physiological appearance of bone in the vertebral column and rib cage of a carcass/side (see Figure 14). Special attention is given to the thoracic vertebrae. Bone maturity is classified as A, B, C, D, and E (youngest to oldest). Some emphasis is placed on color of lean, but usually in young A maturity beef (most of the beef going into the retail self service sales case trade is of A maturity) the color of lean usually varies little (i.e., it is bright cherry-red). Occasionally, depending upon seasonal and management situations, dark cutters (purple) of the lean, a carcass can be dropped as much as one full quality grade. Fortunately, dark cutting beef

rarely happens (<1.5%), but when it does, it is costly. Bullocks (young bulls) and heifers are more susceptible to dark cutting beef syndrome than steers. However, as a beef animal matures, the flesh naturally becomes darker. Usually, in older carcasses (cows) have maturities of C, D, and E, but in some older carcasses the color of lean can be of A maturity (bright cherry red). Lean color can compensate for bone maturity, but usually a C maturity carcass cannot be made an A or B carcass even though the lean is much younger in color. Color of lean of older maturities is of little importance, however, as the lean from these carcasses will be used mostly for the purpose of manufacturing ground beef and sausages. In these cases, when color of lean in the ribeye is not equivalent to the maturity, the color of lean equally compensates for an equal change in skeletal maturity, and vice versa, within certain limitations. Various maturities are described as follows:

a.   <u>A Maturity</u>

Chine bones (bodies of cervical, thoracic, lumbar, and sacral vertebrae) are soft, red, and porous. Cartilage tips on thoracic vertebrae are soft and white. Rib bones are narrow and tend to be round. Sacral vertebrae are only partially ossified. Cartilage tips on lumbar vertebrae are only moderately ossified (hardened to bone). The age of this maturity group is approximately 9 to 30 months. The lean is of a bright cherry-red color. This is the maturity, classified as A, of most beef going to wholesalers, retail stores, institutions, and high-quality restaurants.

b.   <u>B Maturity</u>

Chine bones are slightly hard and tinged with red. Cartilage tips on thoracic vertebrae are slightly ossified. Several lumbar vertebrae are completely fused. Cartilage of the sacral vertebrae is completely ossified. The lean is described as a cherry-red color. The age group of this maturity group range from 30 to 42 months. This maturity is classified as B maturity. Because a small percentage (<5%) of cattle are of B maturity and their commercial value is decreased if they do not have a minimum modest degree of marbling.

c.   <u>C Maturity</u>

Chine bones are rather white. Cartilage tips on thoracic vertebrae are moderately ossified (approximately 30 to 70%). Lumbar and sacral vertebrae are fully ossified. Lean is usually somewhat darker in color although it can be cherry-red.

The age of this maturity group is about 42 to 72 months. This maturity would be classified as C maturity and contains mainly a class of cattle called heiferettes (may have had a calf). Some middle meats (rib and loins) are used for steaks in economy-type steak houses (restaurants).

d.   D Maturity

Chine bones are white and flinty. Cartilage tips on thoracic vertebrae are almost completely ossified and only an outline of these cartilaginous tips remains. Rib bones are flat, white, and quite wide. The age of this maturity group is about 72 to 96 months. This is the D maturity category. This maturity contains bulls, beef and dairy cows considered nonproductive.

e.   E Maturity

These very mature carcasses have hard, white, flinty bones. Cartilage on thoracic vertebrae is completely ossified and the outlines of these tips are not visible. Lean is dark in color. The age of the maturity group is over 96 months and is considered the oldest maturity, E maturity. C, D, and E maturities include breeding stock which are no longer considered economically valuable in herds. Meat from E maturity carcasses is used for manufacturing purposes (grinding and sausage).

Figure 14. Location of various areas of vertebral column used in determining maturity of a beef carcass.

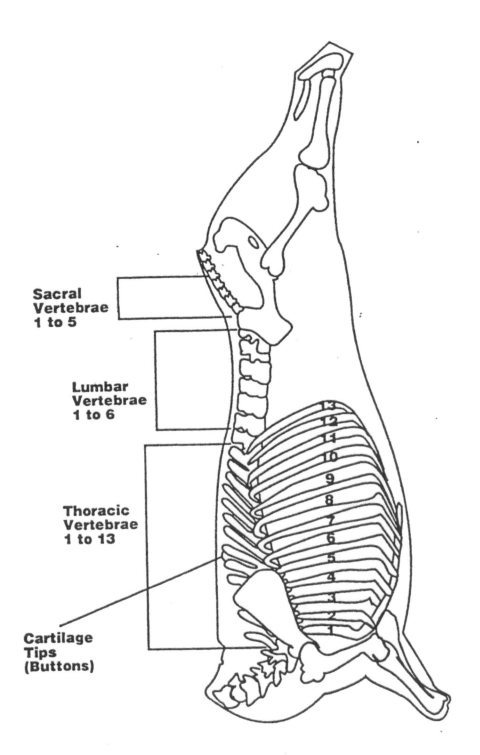

Sacral
Vertebrae
1 to 5

Lumbar
Vertebrae
1 to 6

Thoracic
Vertebrae
1 to 13

Cartilage
Tips
(Buttons)

2. Marbling (intramuscular fat)

a. Defined as small pieces (flecks) of intramuscular fat within the lean area of the ribeye as visually observed in the cross-section of the ribeye (longissimus thoracis) between the 12th and 13th ribs.

b. USDA degrees of marbling (see Figure 15) in a ribeye (from most to least) and lower and upper limits within a degree of marbling (0–100) as follows:

1) Abundant (Ab$^{0-100}$)
2) Moderately abundant (MdA$^{0-100}$)
3) Slightly abundant (SlA$^{0-100}$)
4) Moderate (Md$^{0-100}$)
5) Modest (Mt$^{0-100}$)
6) Small (Sm$^{0-100}$)
7) Slight (Sl$^{0-100}$)
8) Traces (Tr$^{0-100}$)
9) Practically devoid

3. Market cattle marble (deposit intramuscular fat) differently depending upon genetics, maturity, sex, and management. Under normal feeding regimens, genetics exert a significant role in marbling deposition. Certain breed and breed types such as Angus and Angus-cross cattle have a higher propensity to marble than the newer, larger-framed exotic and exotic cross cattle. In general, Angus, along with Holsteins, are known to marble (more likely to grade average and high Choice and Prime); whereas, Herefords, bullocks, and exotic breeds and their crosses usually have traces, slight, and small degrees of marbling (Standard, Select, and low Choice, respectively) when fed a high-energy ration and marketed 12 to 18 months of age. Heifers have a tendency to deposit intramuscular fat earlier than steers and, consequently, quality grade higher.

Figure 15.   Illustrations of the lower limits for marbling within six marbling degrees of USDA quality grades of beef carcasses. Courtesy of National Live Stock and Meat Board and United States Department of Agriculture.

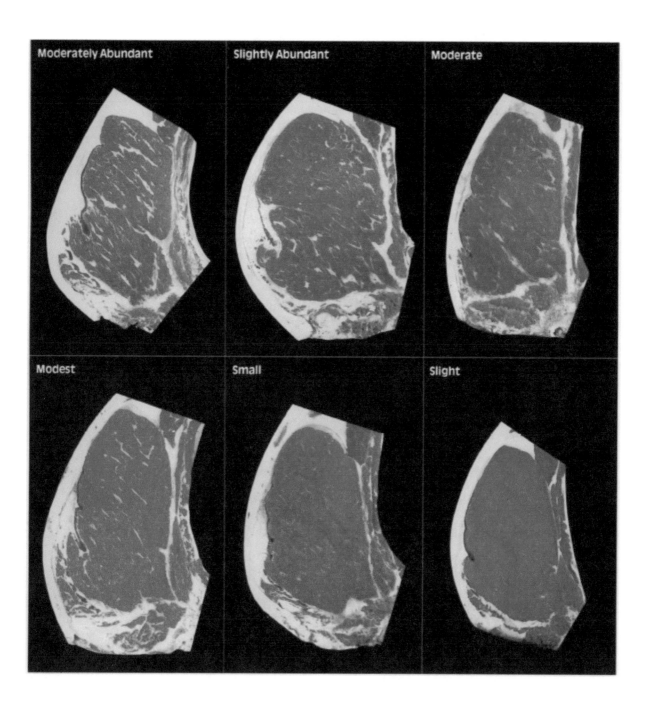

H. Determination of the relationship between maturity and marbling, and quality grade (see Figure 16).

1. First determine maturity of a carcass by observing stage of bone and lean maturity.

2. Next the amount (degree), distribution and texture of marbling are determined. The amount or degree is the most important consideration of these three in determining quality grade of beef carcasses.

3. "A" maturity carcasses with

    a. Slightly abundant, moderately abundant and abundant degrees of marbling are eligible for US low (Pr^-), average (Pr°) and high Prime (Pr^+), respectively.

    b. Small, modest and moderate degrees of marbling quality for US low (Ch^-), average Ch°) and high Choice (Ch^+), respectively.

    c. Slight degree of marbling will qualify for US Select, (Slight 50–100 qualifies for high select (Se^+) and slight 0–49 qualifies for low select (Se^-).

    d. Practically devoid and traces degrees of marbling will qualify for low (Std^-) and high Standard (Std^+), respectively. In B maturity carcasses, small, slight and traces degrees of marbling will grade high Standard, and practically devoid will grade low Standard.

4. Stage of maturity and degree of marbling are correlated using the information shown in Figure 16. For example, if a carcass is determined to be A^{50} (about 14 to 16 months) and has a small degree of marbling, then the USDA quality grade would be low Choice.

5. In actual practice, the USDA grader in commercial plants will stamp or roll (a grade mark) a carcass US Prime, Choice, or Select. Carcasses qualifying for US Select, Standard, Commercial and Utility, but are not rolled with a grade mark are commonly referred to as "no rolls." USDA quality and yield grading is a voluntary service and paid for by the user.

Figure 16.

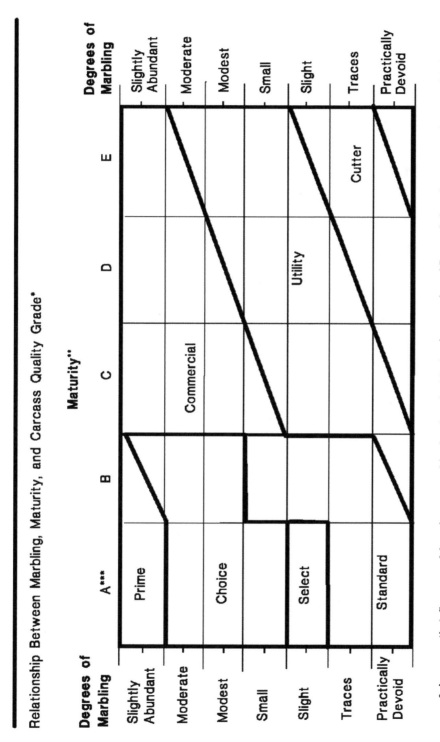

Relationship Between Marbling, Maturity, and Carcass Quality Grade*

* Assumes that firmness of lean is comparably developed with the degree of marbling and that the carcass is not a "dark cutter."

** Maturity increases from left to right (A through E).

*** The A maturity portion of the Figure is the only portion applicable to bullock carcasses.

47

I. Determination of Yield Grade for Beef Carcasses

1. USDA yield grades signify, using numbers 1 through 5, the proportion of a carcass that can be fabricated into closely trimmed retail cuts from the chuck, rib, loin, and round (see Table 4). A yield grade 1 (a very lean muscular animal) represents a high cutability, and the number 5 (usually an excessively fat animal) represents a low cutability carcass. Hence, the relationship between yield grade and cutability is an inverse one. Cutability is defined as the ratio or proportion of retail cut weight to carcass weight. It is usually reported as a percentage. Data in Table 4 illustrates the differences in percentage yield of closely trimmed cuts from the chuck, rib, loin, and round for yield grades to a tenth of a yield grade. Most carcasses marketed today would have a yield grade of 3, although the trend is to greater leanness and consequently, lower yield grade numbers. For example, a carcass with a yield grade of 3.0 would have a 50 percent yield of cuts; whereas, a yield grade 4.0 carcass would have a 47.7 percent yield of cuts. A difference in yield grade also means a difference in economic value. Today many packers are using pricing grids to discount/reward value. It is not unusual for yield grade 4 carcasses to be worth $10 to $14 less per cwt than yield grade 3's and lower. Carcasses over 900 pounds and under 575 pounds may also be discounted. Consequently, it is of economic significance to produce high cutability market beef within an acceptable weight range. As a general rule, large-framed animals have lower yield grade numbers (higher cutability) whereas small-framed animals have higher yield grade numbers (lower cutability) at a constant weight.

2. Yield grade is determined by using four factors: 1) fat thickness over the ribeye; 2) ribeye area; 3) carcass weight; and 4) kidney, pelvic, and heart fat. An equation has been determined from scientific data for determining yield grades of beef carcasses and is as follows:

Yield Grade = 2.5 + 2.5 (fat thickness, inches)

+ 0.2 (percent kidney, pelvic and heart fat)

+ .0038 (hot carcass weight, pounds)

- .32 (ribeye area, square inches)

Table 4. Relationship of yield grade to percentage yield of cuts.

Yield Grade	Yield of Cuts	Yield Grade	Yield of Cuts
1.0	54.6	3.5	48.9
1.1	54.4	3.6	48.7
1.2	54.2	3.7	48.4
1.3	53.9	3.8	48.2
1.4	53.7	3.9	48.0
1.5	53.5	4.0	47.7
1.6	53.3	4.1	47.5
1.7	53.0	4.2	47.3
1.8	52.8	4.3	47.0
1.9	52.6	4.4	46.8
2.0	52.3	4.5	46.6
2.1	52.1	4.6	46.4
2.2	51.9	4.7	46.1
2.3	51.6	4.8	45.9
2.4	51.4	4.9	45.7
2.5	51.2	5.0	45.4
2.6	51.0	5.1	45.2
2.7	50.7	5.2	45.0
2.8	50.5	5.3	44.7
2.9	50.3	5.4	44.5
3.0	50.0	5.5	44.3
3.1	49.8	5.6	44.1
3.2	49.6	5.7	43.8
3.3	49.3	5.8	43.6
3.4	49.1	5.9	43.3

The grader, however, does not use this equation in commercial practice, but rather bases his/her decisions on previous training and experience to yield grade a carcass to a whole yield grade. Camera grading is used in many commercial plants today to estimate fat thickness and ribeye area.   Graders may also, however, use a short cut method of determining yield grade from the yield grade equation to simplify calculations and expedite yield grading.

3. The process of estimating yield grade
    a. First determine a preliminary yield grade (PYG) by estimating or measuring the fat covering over the ribeye (see Figure 16). For example, .4 inches of fat at the 12–13th rib would be equivalent to a PYG of 3.0 as illustrated in the following:

FT and PYG Relationship

Thickness of Fat	PYG
.2	2.5
.4	3.0
.6	3.5
.8	4.0
1.0	4.5
1.2	5.0

Note: PYG may be adjusted, either upward or downward as necessary to reflect unusual deposits of fat on other parts of the carcass (lower rib, outside and inside rounds, brisket, cod/udder).

    b. Next: estimate or measure the area of the ribeye (see Figure 13). Estimation of ribeye area for live market animals is based on an estimated carcass weight (DP times live weight results in hot carcass weight). A certain ribeye area is required for a particular hot carcass weight (See Table 4). Use this ribeye area as a starting point in estimating ribeye area. The adjustment for area of ribeye in relation to weight is as follows: For each square inch more than the ribeye area indicated in the hot carcass weight-area of ribeye schedule (see Table 3), subtract 0.3 of a grade from the PYG. For each square inch less than the area indicated in the weight-area of ribeye schedule, add 0.3 of a grade to PYG. This adjustment would be made for an animal/carcass lacking muscularity.

    c. Estimate the percentage of kidney, pelvic and heart fat (KPH). The adjustment for percent KPH is as follows: For each percent of KPH more than 3.5 percent, add .2 of a yield grade to the PYG. You would make this kind of adjustment for a muscular animal carcass. For each percent of KPH less than 3.5 %, subtract .2 of a grade from the PYG. The following are examples of adjustments for KPH percentages:

Kidney, Pelvic and Heart Fat Adjustment

1.0%	=	-.50
1.5%	=	-.40
2.0%	=	-.30
2.5%	=	-.20
3.0%	=	-.10
3.5%	=	- 0
4.5%	=	+.20

d. Calculate the final yield grade (1–5 to the nearest 0.1 of a yield grade) by adding and/or subtracting the adjustments to or from the PYG.

e. For example, a 700 lb carcass with 0.4 in of fat, a 13.2 square inch ribeye area and 2.0% KPH would have a final yield grade (FYG) of 2.4.

Fat of 0.4 inch = 3.0 PYG

13.2 square inch. ribeye at
700 lbs. needs a 12.2 – = - .3
(therefore, subtract .3 of a YG because more muscular)

2.0% KPH = - .3
(1.5% less than base 3.5%) therefore, subtract .3 of a YG

$$\text{Final YG} = \overline{2.4}$$

4. Another example for the purpose of calculating final yield grade is a 630 lb carcass with 0.8 inch of fat, a 10.0 square inch ribeye and 4.0% kidney knob. This carcass would have a final yield grade (FYG) of 4.5.

Fat of 0.8 inch = 4.0 PYG

10.0 sq. in ribeye at
630 lbs. (needs a 11.3 – = +.4
therefore, add .4 of a YG because of less muscular)

4.0% KPH = +.1
(0.5% more than base 3.5%) therefore add .1
of a YG

$$\text{FYG} = \overline{4.5}$$

J. Although yield grade can be determined objectively (with the exception of percentage kidney knob), a USDA grader basically determines yield grade by using visual judgment. Instead of denoting yield grade as a 0.1 of a yield grade, it is denoted as a whole number within a shield configuration, e.g., USDA Yield Grade 3. The USDA grader, however, may use objective methods of more accurately determining yield grade when carcasses are subject to regrade. When camera systems are in place, YG to the nearest 0.1 YG is calculated.

K. Slaughter cattle and their grades are as follows:

Young Beef (A&B)	Quality Grade	Yield Grade
Steer[a], Heifer[b]	Prime, Choice, Select	1 to 5
Bullock[c]	Standard, Utility	
Heiferette[d]	Choice, Select	1 to 5
	Standard, Utility	
Old Beef (C, D, &E)	Commercial, Utility	
Steer, Heiferette, Cow[e]	Cutter and Canner	

[a] Steer – young male castrate, [b] Heifer – young female,[c] Bullock – young intact male
[d] Heiferette – young female that has calved,[e] Cow – older female

Young beef can be graded for both quality and yield grade or separately graded for quality and yield grade.

L. The systematic process of calculating carcass and live market prices is as follows:
1. Estimate dressing percent (DP) to acquire hot carcass weight (live weight x DP = hot carcass weight)
2. Estimate carcass quality grade to the nearest one-third (or one-half) grade, and calculate yield grade to the nearest 0.1 of a YG.
3. Assume for this example only that for every 0.1 yield grade difference between estimated and base carcass yield grade with a base of 3.2, $1.00 would be added or subtracted from the carcass price per cwt.
4. Wholesale carcass price per cwt based on carcass grades will be provided. For example:

Choice	Select
$110/cwt	$100/cwt

Deduct $1.00 per cwt for heifers.
Deduct $5.00 per cwt for angular carcasses (dairy type conformation)
5. Example and calculations of carcass and live value per cwt.
   a. Example: A 1000 pound live beef steer had an estimated dressing percent of 62. As a result, the carcass weight would be 620 pounds (1000 x .62). The carcass graded low Choice ($110/cwt) and had a yield grade of 2.8 (base yield grade of 3.2). The calculated carcass value per cwt is:
   b. Calculation of carcass value per cwt. Quality grade price + price differential ($1.00/.1 YG) x yield grade difference in tenths) = carcass value/cwt
   $110.00 (carcass price/cwt) + [($1.00 x (3.2-2.8)10] = $114.00 carcass value/cwt
   c. Calculation of live value per cwt.
   Carcass price per cwt ($104) x DP (.62) (as a decimal) = per cwt live value
   $114 x .62 = $70.68 live value/cwt

V. BEEF CARCASS FABRICATION

A. Slaughter (Dressing)
  1. Proper handling, access to water and overnight off feed before slaughter are important practices for securing carcass quality.
  2. Individual animals are restrained and usually stunned by penetrating (captive-bolt) or non-penetrating compression guns. Stunning is done either at the forehead or back of the head depending on the type of stunning device employed.
  3. Sticking (exsanguinations) is accomplished by shackling and hoisting the stunned animal onto an overhead rail. The knife is inserted in front of the brisket at a 45° angle and the carotid arteries and jugular veins are severed.
  4. Hide removal usually occurs as follows:
      a. Heading or skinning out of the head.
      b. Shanking or legging of the fore and hind shanks.
      c. Siding or removal of the hide from the sides.
      d. Backing or removal of the hide from the back is usually done by mechanical equipment.
  5. Evisceration is the process of removal of the internal organs. The brisket and the abdominal cavities are opened by using a knife and the internal organs are systematically removed.
  6. The carcass is halved by sawing down the middle of the vertebral column of the carcass.
  7. After dressing is completed, the halves are washed with potable water by using a high-pressure cabinet.
  8. After weighing, identifying, and inspecting are done, the sides (halves) are rolled into a high air velocity chill cooler.
B. After about a 24 hr. chill both sides are cut (ribbed) between the 12th and 13th ribs so that the ribeye and fat cover are exposed for the purpose of quality and yield grading. Subsequently, the forequarter is separated from the hindquarter at the site of the 12th and 13th rib (termed quartering). The forequarter and hindquarter represents 52 and 48 percent, respectively, of the beef carcass. In the past, most beef was shipped to the retailer as fore and hindquarters (fronts and hinds). Boxed beef represents primal and subprimals, some of which are trimmed and boneless, wrapped under vacuum in an oxygen impermeable package (vacuum packed) and boxed. Consequently, much of the waste products (fat and bone) now remain at the fabrication plat where greater value can be added by producing high quality tallow and bone meal. Also, beef cuts are fabricated and marketed according to USDA Institutional Meat Purchasing Specifications. These specifications facilitate both buying and selling. The National Association of Meat Purveyor's "The Meat Buyers Guide" is an excellent source of information on the

purchase of both wholesale and retail specification cuts. (pp. 57-59 Muscles, Bones, Retail Cuts)

C. Figure 17 shows the location, structure and names of the bones of the beef carcass. Knowledge about bones is helpful in identifying and purchasing retail cuts.

D. Figure 18 provides information about the location of each of the wholesale (primal) cuts of the carcass. The wholesale (primal) cuts will eventually be cut into retail cuts.

E. Figure 19 contains information about the various retail cuts that can be obtained from their respective wholesale cuts, and their recommended methods of cookery. The "Uniform Retail Meat Identity Standards" published by the National Live Stock and Meat Board is an excellent source of information on retail cuts and their cookery. Also, see pp. 92-97 for details about methods of cookery.

F. Forequarter (52 percent of the carcass)

   1. The percentage of each wholesale cut from the forequarter of the beef carcass is as follows:

Wholesale Cut	% of Carcass
Chuck	27
Rib	10
Plate	8
Brisket	4
Shank	3
Total	52

Figure 17. Beef Bones

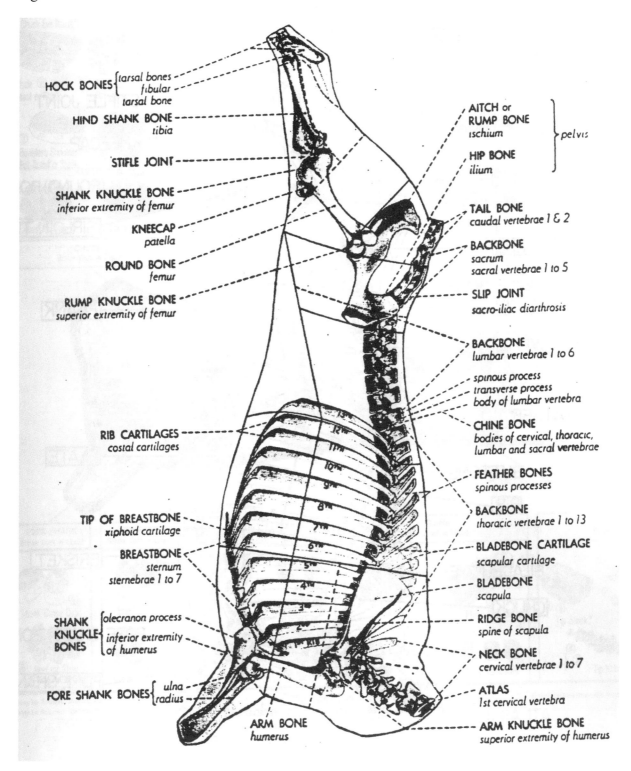

HOCK BONES { tarsal bones
              fibular
              tarsal bone

HIND SHANK BONE
  tibia

STIFLE JOINT

SHANK KNUCKLE BONE
  inferior extremity of femur

KNEECAP
  patella

ROUND BONE
  femur

RUMP KNUCKLE BONE
  superior extremity of femur

RIB CARTILAGES
  costal cartilages

TIP OF BREASTBONE
  xiphoid cartilage

BREASTBONE
  sternum
  sternebrae 1 to 7

SHANK
KNUCKLE { olecranon process
BONES   inferior extremity
           of humerus

FORE SHANK BONES { ulna
                   radius

ARM BONE
  humerus

AITCH or
RUMP BONE
  ischium   } pelvis

HIP BONE
  ilium

TAIL BONE
  caudal vertebrae 1 & 2

BACKBONE
  sacrum
  sacral vertebrae 1 to 5

SLIP JOINT
  sacro-iliac diarthrosis

BACKBONE
  lumbar vertebrae 1 to 6

spinous process
transverse process
body of lumbar vertebra

CHINE BONE
  bodies of cervical, thoracic,
  lumbar and sacral vertebrae

FEATHER BONES
  spinous processes

BACKBONE
  thoracic vertebrae 1 to 13

BLADEBONE CARTILAGE
  scapular cartilage

BLADEBONE
  scapula

RIDGE BONE
  spine of scapula

NECK BONE
  cervical vertebrae 1 to 7

ATLAS
  1st cervical vertebra

ARM KNUCKLE BONE
  superior extremity of humerus

Figure 18. Beef Wholesale Cuts

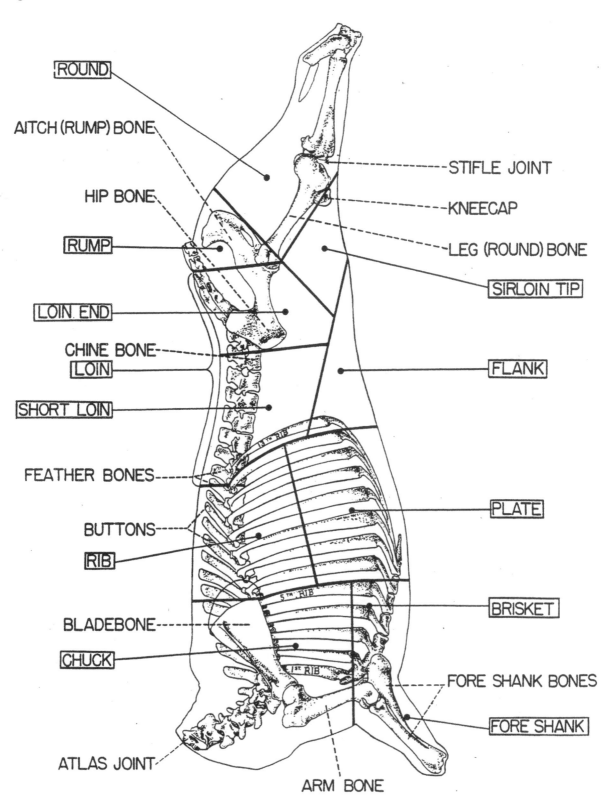

Figure 19. Beef Retail Cuts

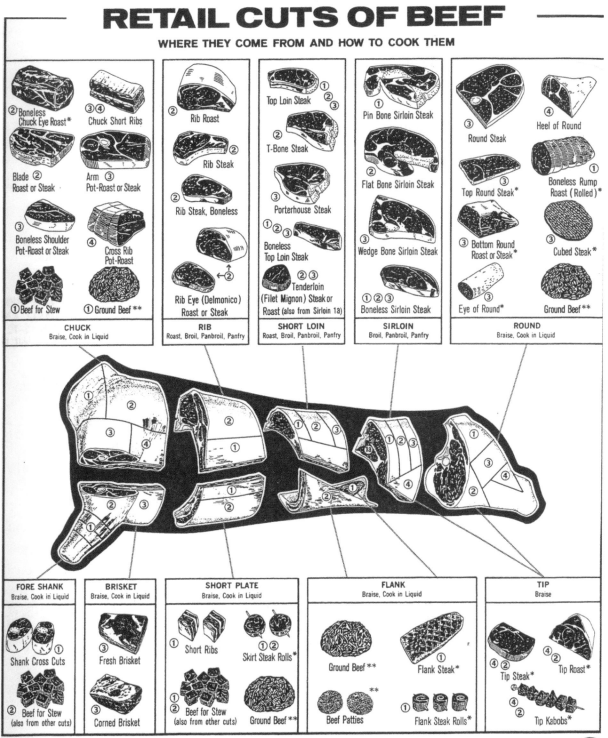

2. Fabrication of forequarter (See Figure 17) into wholesale primal and retail cuts is as follows:

    a. The wholesale rib and plate are cut from the wholesale chuck, brisket and shank between the fifth and sixth ribs and perpendicular to the back.

    b. The wholesale rib is separated from the wholesale plate by cutting about 10 inches or less from the chine parallel to the back. The typical retail cuts are:

        1. Rib steaks (contains longissimus thoracis (ribeye) and spinalis dorsi (cap muscle), thoracic vertebrae and rib bone). The boneless rib steaks are called ribeye steaks.

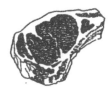

Beef Rib Steak Small End
Rib 11-12
(Broil, Panbroil, Panfry)

Beef Rib Steak Small End BNLS
Rib 11-12
(Broil, Panbroil, Panfry)

        2. Rib roast (contains thoracic vertebrae, ribs, and several muscles including the longissimus, spinalis dorsi, latissimus dorsi and trapezius, as well as layers of seam fat). Usually rib roasts are cut from the large end (anterior) of the wholesale rib.

BEEF RIB ROAST LARGE END
Ribs 6–8
(Roast)

    c. The wholesale (primal) chuck is removed from the brisket and shank by a cut parallel to the back of the chuck at the distal end of the humerus (arm) bone (begin the cut at the angle of the forearm and cut parallel to the back). Typical retail cuts from the chuck are:

        1. Blade steaks and blade roasts (contains blade bones [scapula]). 7-bone steak and roast is identified by shape of the blade bone as the number 7. Contains infraspinatus, supraspinatus, serratus ventralis, and subscapularis).

BEEF CHUCK
POT-ROAST BNLS
(Braise)

BEEF CHUCK
7-BONE POT-ROAST
(Braise)

2. Arm steaks and arm roasts (identified by arm bone [humerus]) and has triceps brachii, biceps brachii, and deep pectoral as major muscles.

BEEF CHUCK
ARM STEAK
(Braise)

  d. With today's boxed beef trade, retailers will cut retail cuts from a three-piece chuck rather than a wholesale chuck.
  e. See Figure 17 for the remainder of the retail cuts that can be obtained from the wholesale cuts of the forequarter, and for their method of cookery.
G. Hindquarter (48% of the carcass)
  1. The percentage of each wholesale cut from the hindquarter of the beef carcass is as follows:

Wholesale Cut	% of Carcass
Round	23
Sirloin (Loin end)	9
Short Loin	8
Flank	5
Kidney knob and hanging tender	3
Total	48

  2. Fabrication of the hindquarter (see Figure 18) into wholesale (primal) and retail cuts is as follows.
    a. Initially the hanging tender (part of the diaphragm muscle) and kidney knob are removed. In the past, about 0.5 inch of fat was left of cover on the tenderloin, but today little fat is left on it.
    b. The wholesale flank is removed next by making an angular cut by following the contour of the round (this includes removal of the cod or udder fat) and

cutting across the 13th rib at a point about 10 inches or less from the backbone on the anterior end of the loin (rib end).

c. Formerly, the wholesale round was removed by using three different styles. These were:

    1. The Chicago round which includes half of the sirloin tip.

    2. The New York round which includes none of the tip.

    3. The Diamond round includes the entire tip. The Chicago style round is made by cutting on a line between the last sacral vertebrae and the first coccygeal and about 1.5 inches anterior to the aitch bone. Thus, the sirloin tip will be cut in half, and a piece of the femur (about the size of a silver dollar) will result when the round is removed Chicago style.

    4. In a boxed beef program, the round is separated into three subprimals, a top round, gooseneck round, and sirloin tip.

    5. The subprimals obtained from the round are:

        a. Rump – usually merchandised at retail as a boneless rump roast.

        b. Sirloin tip or knuckle – merchandised at retail both as a steak or roast.

        c. Top (inside) round – usually merchandised as top round steaks. These are very lean.

        d. Bottom (outside) round - merchandised at retail as a bottom round steak (biceps femoris and semitendinosus or biceps femoris alone) and as an eye of round steak (semitendinosus).

        e. Heel or Pike's peak – merchandised at retail as a roast

        f. A "full cut" round steak consists of three major muscles; semimembranosus (top round, semitendinosus (eye of round), and biceps femoris (bottom round). The femur (round bone) is present.

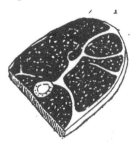

BEEF ROUND STEAK
(Braise, Panfry)

d. The wholesale loin is composed of two subprimals, the short-loin and the sirloin (loin end). The short loin is separated from the sirloin between the fifth and sixth lumbar vertebrae and at the anterior edge of the hipbone. Both the short loin and sirloin (loin end) are fabricated into high quality steaks. Proceeding from the anterior to the posterior end of the wholesale loin the following steaks can be identified.

    1. The short loin is fabricated into the following high quality steaks.

        a. Club steak (may or may not have 13th rib; has the longissimus lumborus and a touch of the psoas major [tenderloin]).

b. A T-bone steak has the T-shape of lumbar vertebrae and has the psoas major (tenderloin) and longissimus (loin eye). A T-bone steak is defined as having a diameter across the center of the tenderloin of no less than ½ inch. As indicated below, the "tail", lip-on, or flange portion of the steak can vary in length and is usually removed entirely in today's modern retail meat merchandising case.

c. A Porterhouse steak has the T-shape of the lumbar vertebrae and

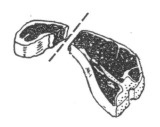

BEEF LOIN
T-BONE STEAK
(Broil, Panbroil, Panfry)

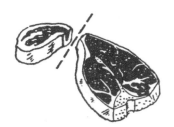

BEEF LOIN
PORTERHOUSE STEAK
(Broil, Panbroil, Panfry)

psoas major (tenderloin), longissimus lumborum, and may have a small segment of gluteus medius. A Porterhouse steak is defined as having a diameter across the center of the tenderloin of 1 ¼ inches and greater. The tail or ventral part of this steak may vary in length. Today it is not unusual for steaks to be displayed in many retail display sale cases with the tail, flange, or lip-on entirely removed.

e. The subprimal sirloin can be fabricated into the steaks taking their name from the configuration of the hipbone (ilium). They are as follows:

1. A pin bone sirloin steak has three major muscles. They are the psoas major (tenderloin), longissimus lumborum (loin eye) and gluteus medius. The two bones are the lumbar vertebrae and the ilium (hip bone).

BEEF LOIN
SIRLOIN STK* PIN BONE
(Broil, Panbroil, Panfry)

61

2. A flat or double bone sirloin steak has three major muscles. They are the psoas major, iliascus (both of these from butt tender), and gluteus medius. A flat bone sirloin steak has only the ilium (hip bone), whereas the double bone has both the ilium (hip) bone and the lumbar vertebrae.

3. A round bone sirloin steak has 3 major muscles. They are the psoas major, gluteus medius, and biceps femoris. The two major bones are the sacral vertebrae and the shaft of the ilium, which is round.

4. A wedge bone sirloin steak has three major muscles. They are the psoas major (tenderloin), gluteus medius (top sirloin), and biceps femoris. The bones are the sacral vertebrae, and the shaft of the ilium, which is shaped like a wedge.

BEEF LOIN
SIRLOIN STK* FLAT BONE
(Broil, Panbroil, Panfry)

BEEF LOIN
SIRLOIN STK* ROUND BONE
(Broil, Panbroil, Panfry)

BEEF LOIN
SIRLOIN STK* WEDGE BONE
(Broil, Panbroil, Panfry)

f. An alternate method of fabricating the wholesale loin is to:
    a. Remove the entire tenderloin for filet mignon steaks (consists of the psoas major and minor muscles).
    b. The loin muscle can be removed as boneless (bnls) or partially boneless as:
        1. A New York strip steak or top loin steak (bone-in strip) (longissimus muscle mainly).
        2. Kansas City strip or top loin steak (boneless strip steak) (longissimus muscle mainly)

BEEF LOIN
TOP LOIN STEAK BNLS*
(Broil, Panbroil, Panfry)

c. The gluteus medius (major muscle of the sirloin or loin end) is cut into boneless top sirloin steaks.

BEEF LOIN
TOP SIRLOIN STEAK BNLS
(Broil, Panbroil, Panfry)

g. Ground beef is major beef product (about 50% of beef is consumed in some form of ground and/or processed product). Ground beef is made from trimmings from the fabrication of retail cuts or in many instance lean from carcasses of cows or grass fed beef is separated from bones and utilized in the manufacture of ground beef.

h. See Figure 19 for other retail cuts obtained from the wholesale cuts of the hindquarter, and their recommended method of cookery.

VI. PORK CARCASS FABRICATION

A. Slaughter (Dressing)
   1. Proper handling, access to water, and off feed overnight prior to slaughter is important to pork carcass quality.
   2. Market hogs are immobilized, or rendered unconscious by electrical stunning or exposure to carbon dioxide.
   3. Sticking, or exsanguination, is accomplished after stunning by inserting a six inch knife, sharpened on both sides of the tip, into an opening of the neck and severing the carotid arteries and jugular veins.
   4. Removal of the hair is usually accomplished by first placing the carcass in a scalding vat containing about 143°F water.
   5. A dehairing machine equipped with belt scrapers attached to rotary bars are used to remove the hair. Hot water is sprayed on the carcass during dehairing. Extreme care is taken to make sure all hair is removed. Small hairs that remain are removed by singeing with a propane torch.
   6. The head is removed at the atlas joint.
   7. Evisceration takes place by opening the abdominal cavity and removing the internal organs.
   8. Leaf fat along the abdominal wall is removed.
   9. After the sides are weighed, identified, washed and inspected, they are moved to a chill cooler.
B. Pork carcasses as split sides are chilled after slaughter for about 24 hours before cutting. About 1/3 of the pork carcass will be cut and sold as fresh cuts and the remaining 2/3 will be cut for further processing- curing and smoking. Slaughter and fabrication of pork has essentially always occurred within the same plant. That is, pork is shipped either as fresh or processed wholesale cuts from the slaughter/fabrication plant. Of the three red meat species, smoking and curing of cuts are most unique to pork and, therefore, pork offers more variety.

C. Figure 20 shows the location and names of the bones of the pork carcass. Knowledge of bones is very valuable in the identification of retail cuts. (pp. Muscles, Bones, and Retail Cuts)

D. Figure 21 provides information about the wholesale (primal) cuts of pork and the location of each.

E. Figure 22 contains information about the various retail cuts that can be obtained from their respective wholesale cuts and the recommended methods of cookery (pp. 92-97, Cookery Methods).

F. Wholesale cuts of pork

   1. Percentage of each wholesale cut derived from the carcass:

Wholesale Cut	% of Carcass
Ham	22
Loin	16
Belly	13
Picnic Shoulder	9
Boston Butt	9
Spare ribs, jowl, feet, neck bones	14
Fat trim	17
Total	100

Figure 20. Pork Bones

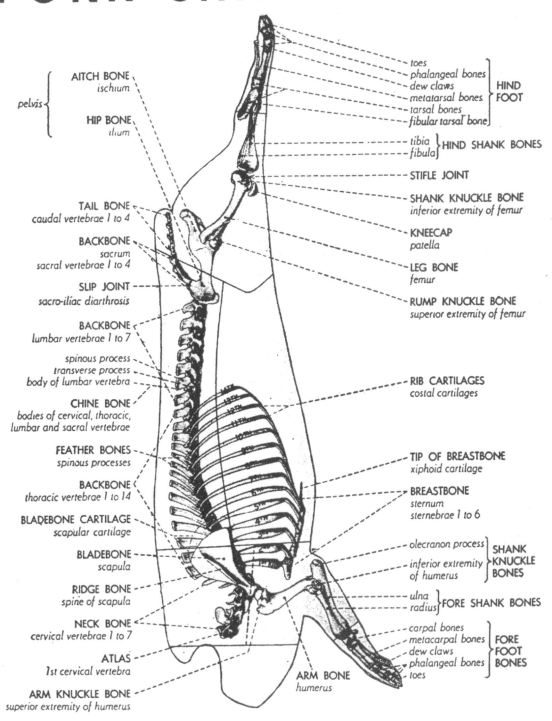

PORK CHART
Location, Structure and Names of Bones

pelvis
AITCH BONE
ischium

HIP BONE
ilium

toes
phalangeal bones
dew claws
metatarsal bones
tarsal bones
fibular tarsal bone
HIND FOOT

tibia
fibula
HIND SHANK BONES

STIFLE JOINT

SHANK KNUCKLE BONE
inferior extremity of femur

KNEECAP
patella

LEG BONE
femur

RUMP KNUCKLE BONE
superior extremity of femur

TAIL BONE
caudal vertebrae 1 to 4

BACKBONE
sacrum
sacral vertebrae 1 to 4

SLIP JOINT
sacro-iliac diarthrosis

BACKBONE
lumbar vertebrae 1 to 7

spinous process
transverse process
body of lumbar vertebra

CHINE BONE
bodies of cervical, thoracic,
lumbar and sacral vertebrae

FEATHER BONES
spinous processes

BACKBONE
thoracic vertebrae 1 to 14

BLADEBONE CARTILAGE
scapular cartilage

BLADEBONE
scapula

RIDGE BONE
spine of scapula

NECK BONE
cervical vertebrae 1 to 7

ATLAS
1st cervical vertebra

ARM KNUCKLE BONE
superior extremity of humerus

RIB CARTILAGES
costal cartilages

TIP OF BREASTBONE
xiphoid cartilage

BREASTBONE
sternum
sternebrae 1 to 6

olecranon process
inferior extremity
of humerus
SHANK KNUCKLE BONES

ulna
radius
FORE SHANK BONES

carpal bones
metacarpal bones
dew claws
phalangeal bones
toes
FORE FOOT BONES

ARM BONE
humerus

Figure 21. Pork Wholesale Cuts

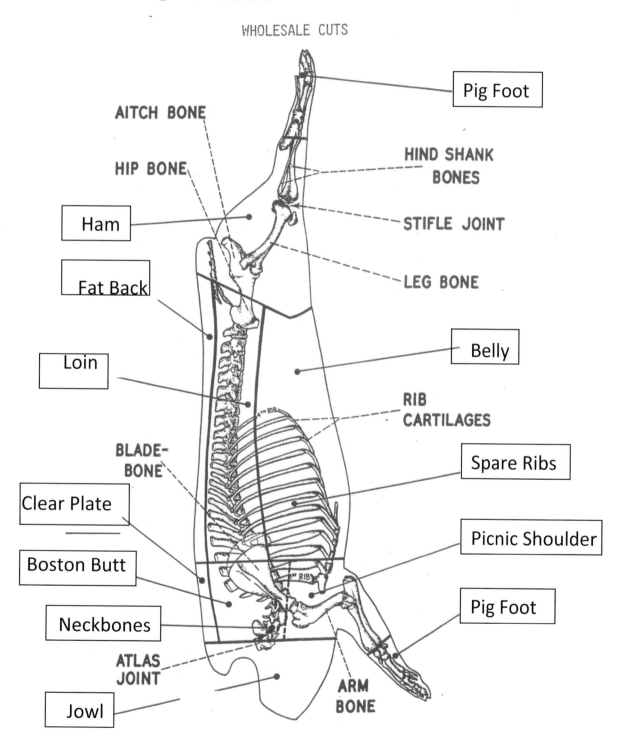

PORK CHART

WHOLESALE CUTS

Pig Foot

AITCH BONE

HIND SHANK BONES

HIP BONE

STIFLE JOINT

Ham

LEG BONE

Fat Back

Belly

Loin

RIB CARTILAGES

BLADE-BONE

Spare Ribs

Clear Plate

Picnic Shoulder

Boston Butt

Pig Foot

Neckbones

ATLAS JOINT

ARM BONE

Jowl

Figure 22. Retail Cuts of Pork

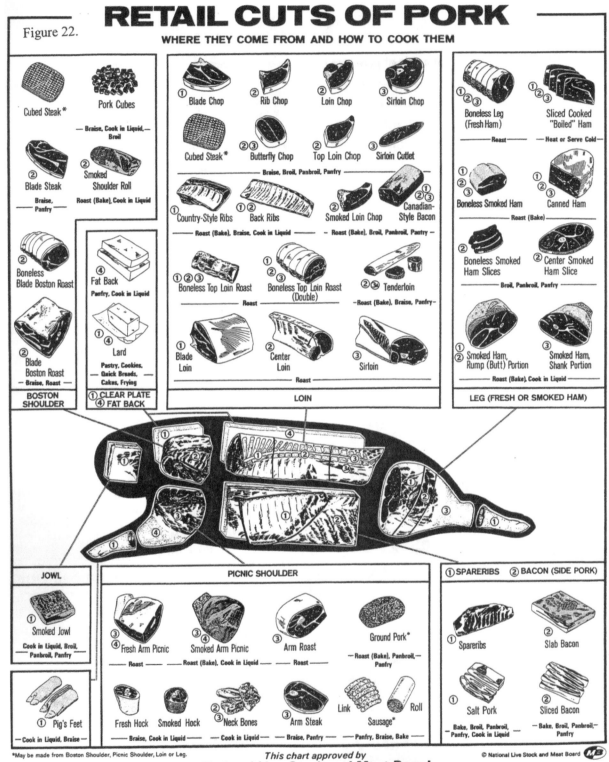

68

G. Fabrication of a side of pork (see Figure 21 and 22) into wholesale and retail cuts, respectively.
   1. The hind and fore feet (only fore feet used for pickled pigs feet) are removed at the hock and knee joints, respectively.
   2. The leg (ham) is removed by making a cut about 2.5 inches anterior to the aitch bone and perpendicular to the long axis of the ham (usually cut between the third and fourth sacral vertebrae). The ham is skinned (skin and fat removed) about ¾ of the distance from the rump face. It is usually cured and smoked. Typical retail cuts obtained from the wholesale ham are:
      a. Fresh ham or fresh butt and shank portions.
      b. Cured as whole, butt and shank portions or boneless. Today many hams are cured and smoked as boneless hams.
      c. Center ham slices, cut about ½ inch in thickness, come from the meatiest part of the ham and contain a portion of the femur bone, and the biceps femoris, semimembranosus, semitendinosus and quadriceps group muscles.

SMOKED HAM WHOLE
(Roast (Bake))

**SMOKED HAM
SHANK PORTION**
(Roast (Bake))

**SMOKED HAM
RUMP PORTION**
(Roast (Bake))

**SMOKED HAM
CENTER SLICES**
(Broil, Panbroil, Panfry,
Roast (Bake))

3. The pork loin is separated from the shoulder by cutting between the 1st and 2nd or even the 2nd and 3rd ribs (depending on the pork chop demand) and at a right angle to the b ack of the carcass. The loin is separated from the belly and spareribs at a point just distal to the blade bone on the anterior end and at the distal edge of tenderloin on the posterior end of the loin. Fatback is trimmed from the back of the loin. Typical retail cuts obtained from the wholesale loin are:
   a. Center loin chops contain the backbone shaped as a T, and have the psoas major and longissimus muscles.
   b. Rib chops have the longissimus and rib bones.
   c. Sirloin chops and roasts are from the sirloin or posterior end of the loin. They contain the backbone, pelvic and hip bones.
   d. Blade end chops and roasts from the blade end or anterior end of the loin contain several muscles, layers of seam fat, and a part of the blade (scapula) bone.
   e. Canadian bacon is a boneless pork loin that has been cured and smoked, and shaped into a compact roll.
   f. A Windsor chop is a pork chop that comes from a cured and smoked loin.
   g. Country style ribs are made by splitting lengthwise the blade end of the loin into halves.
   h. Back ribs are meaty cuts from the blade and/or center loin portion. A longitudinal cut is made about half the thickness of the longissimus muscle, and the muscle remains attached to the rib bones.
   i. Iowa chops are fresh, thick cut (1 ¼ inch thick) center cut pork chops.
   j. The tenderloin is principally the psoas major muscle removed from the loin.
   k. There are three pork trademark cuts:
      1. America's cut is a boneless, 1 ¼ inch thick center loin chop
      2. The Chef's Prime is a boneless chop from the anterior end pork loin.
      3. Chef's Prime filet is a boneless chop from the anterior end pork loin.

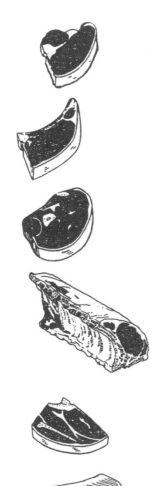

PORK LOIN CHOPS
(Braise, Broil, Panbroil,
Panfry)

**PORK LOIN
RIB CHOPS***
(Braise, Broil, Panbroil,
Panfry)

**PORK LOIN
SIRLOIN CHOPS**
(Braise, Broil, Panbroil,
Panfry)

**PORK LOIN
CENTER RIB ROAST**
(Roast)

**PORK LOIN
BLADE CHOPS**
(Braise, Broil, Panbroil,
Panfry)

**PORK LOIN
BLADE ROAST**
(Roast)

4. Spareribs are removed from the belly by closely cutting the ribs away from the belly portion. Thus, spare ribs are the rib bones with accompanying meat removed from the belly and between the rib bones.
5. The belly is trimmed to square the ends and remove the teat line.
   a. Slab bacon is the cured and smoked product of a side (belly) pork.
   b. Sliced bacon are thin slices cut from slab bacon.
   c. Salt pork is the addition of salt to a belly (side) and (or) jowl.
6. The pork shoulder is composed of two primal lean cuts, the Boston shoulder (butt) and the picnic shoulder. First, the neck bones are removed from the shoulder then the jowl is removed by cutting across the anterior edge of the shoulder parallel with the cut that separates the shoulder from the loin belly and spareribs. The jowl is then trimmed into a square cut jowl. Usually, the picnic shoulder is merchandised at retail as a cured and smoked picnic. It includes the arm and shank bones.

7. The Boston butt is removed from the picnic by cutting perpendicular to the long axis of the shoulder at a distance of about 1 inch below the ventral edge of the blade bone. (The Boston butt is both a wholesale and retail cut). The Boston butt is merchandised at retail as fresh roasts, or pork (blade) steaks (slices).
8. The clear plate (fat layer) is removed from the Boston butt

H. The primal and four lean cuts are:
1. The ham, loin, belly, picnic shoulder and Boston butt are called the primal cuts of pork.
2. The ham, loin, picnic shoulder and Boston butt are known as the four lean cuts.
3. The ham, belly and picnic shoulder are usually cured and smoked whereas the loin and Boston butt are fabricated into and sold as fresh cuts.

PORK SPARERIBS
(Roast (Bake), Broil,
Cook in Liquid)

PORK SHOULDER
BLADE BOSTON ROAST
(Roast)

I. See Figure 21 for the various retail cuts that can be obtained from their respective wholesale cuts, and how they can be cooked. (Also see pp. 115-120, Cooker Methods)

J. Lard Production
1. Source: Fat trimmed from the pork carcass such as fat back, clear plate, trimming fats and leaf fat are used in lard production.
2. Lard Defined: Lard is the fat rendered from fresh, clean, sound fatty tissues from pork with or without lard or hydrogenated lard. Rendering requires heating not to exceed 240°F, sometimes along with pressures of 30-40 psi, to dissolve fatty tissue and to evaporate moisture.
3. Lard is an excellent shortening.

K. Curing and Smoking
1. Curing ingredients: Curing and smoking of pork cuts offer a wide variety of products. The curing ingredients used in a cured product are salt, sugar, nitrite, sodium ascorbate or erythorbate, and phosphates. Certain amounts of each are dissolved in water to form a curing solution, sometimes called a sweet pickle.
2. Methods of curing
   a. There are a number of curing methods. The most prevalent large scale commercial method is to inject the curing solutions into hams, bellies and shoulders with a mechanized pumping machine. Smaller operations would use stitch and/or artery pumping of hams. All three methods require a pressurized pump.

b. A typical curing mixture for hams is as follows:

Ingredient	lb/100 lb water
Salt (NaCl)	10
Sugar (Sucrose)	6.0
Nitrite (K or Na)	0.062*
Sodium erythorbate	0.22*
Phosphate	2.0*

(*Amount must conform to government regulations)
Hams would be pumped to 25% of their weight with this pickle solution to obtain properly cured meat. Ideal pumping temperature ranges from 40-45°F. One gallon of water at 40°F weighs 8.345 lbs.

c. Dry sugar curing (rubbing the curing ingredients in recommended amounts on primarily the lean surface) is typically used in certain commercial operations, small processor operations and on the farm. The dry cure consists of a mixture of 8 lb salt, 2 lb sugar, 3 oz of sodium nitrate and ¼ oz of sodium nitrite. The length of time in cure is dependent on the thickness of the product. For hams and bacons to be adequately cured, seven days per inch of thickness is required (about 35 days for hams and 14 days for bacons).

3. Thermal processing (cooking and smoking)

a. In a large commercial operation, after the introduction of the curing solution into boneless portions, the cured hams are taken to the mechanical massager (tumbler) and massaged (tumbled) for a certain period of time. Next they are placed in stockinettes and taken to a thermal processing unit (formerly called smokehouse) for cooking and smoking. After curing, bellies are hung on smoke trees and taken to a thermal processing unit for cooking and smoking.

1. Hams are taken to a temperature of about 160°F before being removed from the thermal processor unit.

2. Bacons are removed from the smokehouse after reaching a 140°F temperature.

3. The actual time in smoking of the product is a small part of the time in the thermal processor unit. About one-half hour of smoke is given to bacon and three-quarters to 1 hr of smoke is applied to hams.

4. Hardwood sawdust (oak, hickory) is generally used for production of smoke and when applied gives a characteristic smoked flavor. Liquid smoke can also be used by spraying or atomizing it on the surface of whole products, or can be applied as part of the cure in comminuted products.

5. They are then properly shelled, and then cut into shank and butt portions; and center ham slices if they are bone-in products. If they

are boneless, appropriate size cuts are made. These products are usually vacuum packaged.

6. After proper chilling bacons are cut into slabs or slices, and then usually vacuum packaged.

VII. LAMB CARCASS FABRICATION

A. Slaughter (Dressing)

1. Proper handling prior to slaughter is important to carcass quality. Water, but no feed, should be available overnight.
2. The lamb is restrained and stunning is accomplished by an electrical or compression stunner.
3. The stunned lamb is shackled and hoisted onto an overhead rail. Sticking or bleeding occurs by making a knife cut across the neck at the base of the jaw severing the jugular veins and carotid arteries.
4. Pelting is done by removing the pelt from the fore and hind shanks and body. This is achieved by using a knife and mechanical pelt pulling equipment. Also the skill of fisting (use of the fist) to remove the pelt without breaking the fell (a thin membrane attached to the pelt) is essential in good workmanship of pelt removal.
5. Evisceration removes the internal organs from the carcass. This is always a tedious task in avoiding the cutting of the digestive and/or intestinal tracts.
6. The carcasses are washed, weighed and identified and moved into a cooler to rapidly remove the heat of the carcass.

B. After chilling for about 24 hours the lamb carcass is separated into a foresaddle and a hindsaddle by making a cut between the 12th and 13th ribs. The foresaddle makes up 51 percent and the hindsaddle makes up 49 percent of the carcass. Like beef, it is becoming more popular to box lamb primal and subprimals for sale to retailers.

C. Figure 23 shows the location and names of the bones of the lamb carcass. Knowledge of bone location and names is helpful in identifying and purchasing retail cuts. (pp. 81-83 Muscles, Bones, and Retail Cuts)

D. Figure 24 provides information about the wholesale cuts and the location of each of these cuts. (See pp. 92-97, Cookery Methods.)

E. Figure 25 contains information about the various retail cuts that can be obtained from their respective wholesale cuts, and their recommended methods of cookery.

F. Foresaddle (51 percent of carcass)

1. The percentage of the wholesale cuts from the foresaddle as a percentage of the carcass is as follows:

Wholesale Cut	% of carcass
Shoulder	26
Rib or Rack	10
Foreshank	5
Breast	10
Total	**51**

2. Fabrication of the foresaddle (See Figure 23 and 24) into wholesale and retail cuts, respectively.
   a. The shoulder is separated from the rib between the fourth and fifth ribs and cut perpendicular to the back. The neck is removed from the shoulder by making a straight cut extending from the back. Sawing through the middle of the backbone separates the pair of shoulders. Typical retail cuts from the wholesale shoulder are:
      1. Blade chops contain the blade (scapula) bone and rib bones.
      2. Arm chops have the arm (humerus) bone.
      3. Square-cut shoulder
      4. Boneless shoulder roast

**LAMB SHOULDER
BLADE CHOPS**
(Braise, Broil, Panbroil,
Panfry)

**LAMB SHOULDER
ARM CHOPS**
(Braise, Broil, Panbroil,
Panfry)

**LAMB SHOULDER
SQUARE CUT WHOLE**
(Roast)

**LAMB SHOULDER
ROAST BNLS**
(Roast)

b. Rib or rack typical retail cuts are:
1. Rib chops and rib roasts contain rib bones and principally the longissimus thoracis muscle. Frenched rib chops have some of the fat and lean removed from the ventral part of the rib bone.
2. A crown roast is a fancy roast prepared by removing the backbones and shaping it in the form of a crown.

LAMB RIB ROAST
(Roast)

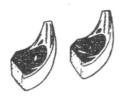

LAMB RIB CHOPS
(Broil, Panbroil, Panfry,
Roast (Bake)

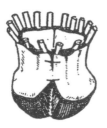

**LAMB RIB
CROWN ROAST**
(Roast)

c. Breasts and shanks are separated from the shoulder by cutting across the arm bone at a point slightly above the knuckle and roughly parallel to the top of the shoulder.

d. See Figure 25 for the various retail cuts that can be obtained from the wholesale cuts of the foresaddle, and how they can be cooked.

Figure 23. Lamb Chart: Location, Structure and Names of Bones

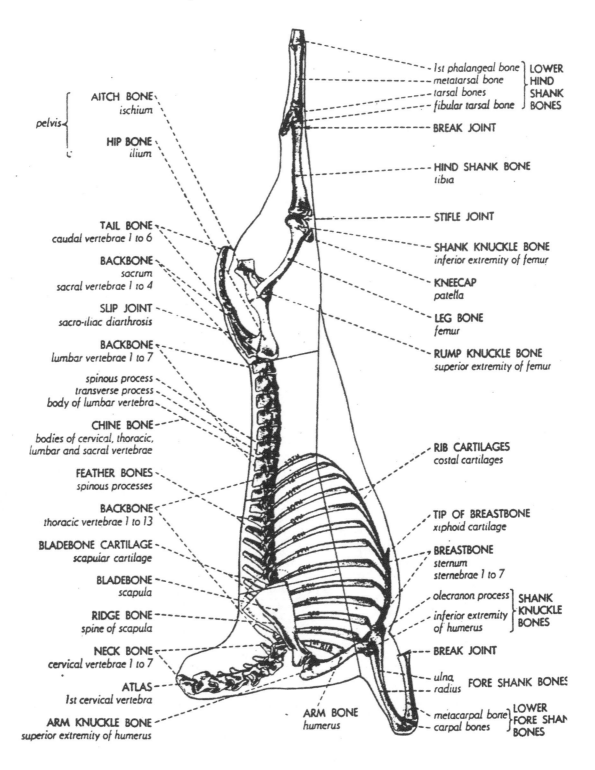

AITCH BONE
ischium

pelvis

HIP BONE
ilium

1st phalangeal bone] LOWER
metatarsal bone   HIND
tarsal bones   SHANK
fibular tarsal bone] BONES

BREAK JOINT

HIND SHANK BONE
tibia

STIFLE JOINT

TAIL BONE
caudal vertebrae 1 to 6

BACKBONE
sacrum
sacral vertebrae 1 to 4

SLIP JOINT
sacro-iliac diarthrosis

BACKBONE
lumbar vertebrae 1 to 7

spinous process
transverse process
body of lumbar vertebra

CHINE BONE
bodies of cervical, thoracic,
lumbar and sacral vertebrae

FEATHER BONES
spinous processes

BACKBONE
thoracic vertebrae 1 to 13

BLADEBONE CARTILAGE
scapular cartilage

BLADEBONE
scapula

RIDGE BONE
spine of scapula

NECK BONE
cervical vertebrae 1 to 7

ATLAS
1st cervical vertebra

ARM KNUCKLE BONE
superior extremity of humerus

SHANK KNUCKLE BONE
inferior extremity of femur

KNEECAP
patella

LEG BONE
femur

RUMP KNUCKLE BONE
superior extremity of femur

RIB CARTILAGES
costal cartilages

TIP OF BREASTBONE
xiphoid cartilage

BREASTBONE
sternum
sternebrae 1 to 7

olecranon process] SHANK
                     KNUCKLE
inferior extremity   BONES
of humerus   ]

BREAK JOINT

ulna   FORE SHANK BONES
radius

ARM BONE
humerus

metacarpal bone] LOWER
                   FORE SHANK
carpal bones   ] BONES

79

Figure 24. Lamb Chart: Wholesale Cuts

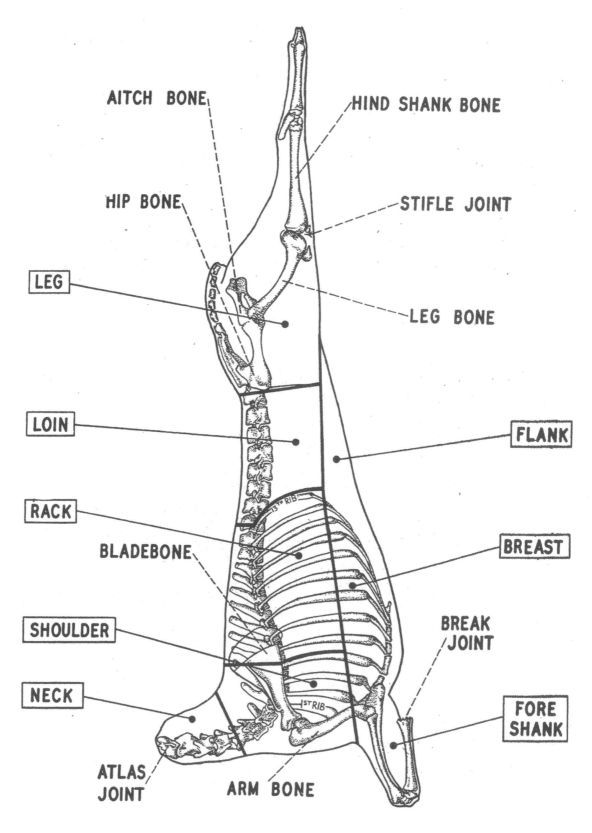

Figure 25. Retail Cuts of Lamb

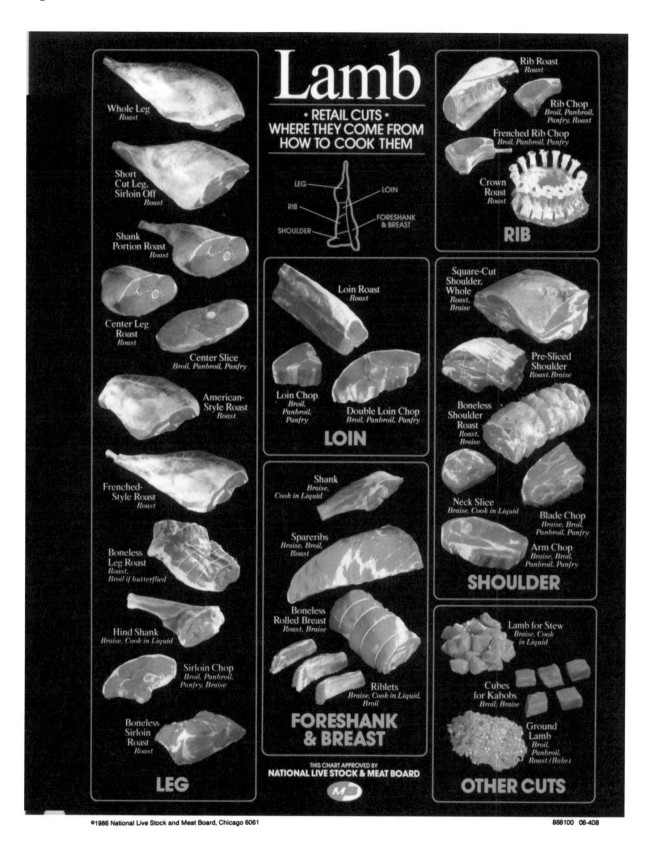

G. Hindsaddle (49% of carcass)

1. Percentage of the wholesale cuts from the hindsaddle as a percentage of the carcass is as follows:

Wholesale Cut	% of Carcass
Leg	34
Loin	11
Flanks	2
Kidney Fat	2
Total	49

2. Fabrication of hindsaddle (See Figure 23) into wholesale and retail cuts.
   a. The flank is removed by cutting two inches ventral to the loin eye and at an angle to the ventral edge of the wholesale leg.
   b. The leg is removed from the loin by making a cut just anterior to the hipbone and perpendicular to the back. In this way the sirloin is included with the leg. The aitch bone is split to separate the legs.
      1. There are three types of leg of lamb: American, Frenched and boneless.
      2. Sirloin chops

**LAMB LEG
AMERICAN STYLE ROAST**
(Roast)

**LAMB LEG
FRENCHED STYLE ROAST**
(Roast)

**LAMB LEG
ROAST BONELESS**
(Roast)

   c. The loin is fabricated into the following retail cuts

1. Loin chops contain the backbone, longissimus, lumborum and the psoas major. Double loin chops can be fabricated by using both sides of the loin.

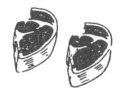

LAMB LOIN CHOPS
(Broil, Panbroil, Panfry)

2. Bone-in and boneless roasts.
3. Sirloin chops contain backbone, pelvic and hipbones, and gluteus medius, longissimus, and biceps femoris.

VIII. POULTRY PROCESSING

A. Dressing Poultry:

1. Poultry should be carefully handled and have free access to water before slaughter. Feed should not be available 8 to 10 hours before slaughter.
2. The approved and most widely practiced method of bleeding birds is cutting of the throat. This method is carried out by shackling the birds by the legs and suspending them on a rail. They are then stunned by an electric current as they pass through a stun cabinet before severing the jugular veins.
3. Scalding is the method most commonly practiced to loosen feathers. The temperature of the water used for scalding is dependent on the maturity and kind of fowl. Semi-scalding is the most popularly used method. Water temperature should be 125°F to 126° F for young, tender skinned birds, 127°F to 128° F for roasters and young turkeys, and 130°F to 132°F for more mature birds. This process takes only 1 ½ to 2 minutes/carcass.
4. Feathers are removed from the carcass by rotary drums or wheels containing long rubber projections ("fingers"). As the carcass is brought in contact with the rubber fingers, feathers loosened by scalding are stripped away with little damage to the skin.
5. Chilling is designed to rapidly and completely reduce carcass temperature. Most chillers use slush ice or ice water to serve as coolants. Agitation of the cooling medium is achieved mechanically. With mechanical, inline chillers, poultry can be cooled to less than 40° F in 30 minutes.
6. Evisceration is the process of removing the internal organs.
7. Refrigeration and Freezing
    a. Chicken is usually refrigerated as whole or parts.
    b. Turkey is usually frozen, although fresh (as opposed to frozen) parts and cuts are becoming more prevalent in the retail sales case.

B. Dressing Percent

1. Fasted overnight shrink will vary from 2-7 percent for chickens and heavy turkeys. .
2. Depending upon the weight and condition of the bird, dressing loss will vary. Chickens under 5 pounds will lose an average of 11 percent blood-and-feather-dressed in contrast to 27 percent full-dressed; whereas chickens over 5 pounds will average 9 to 25 percent losses, respectively. Male turkeys weighing between 13 and 17 pounds and those over 20 pounds will lose an average of 10 and 8 percent blood-and-feather-dressed, respectively. Fully dressed male turkeys will average 18 to 20 percent losses.

C. Grades and Classes

1. The US consumer grades for poultry are US Grade A, Grade B and Grade C. These grades are the ones used at the retail level for consumer recognition, and are the most important of the two types of grades.
2. The US Procurement Grades are US Procurement Grade I and II. These grades are primarily for institutional use.
3. These grades apply to all kinds ("kind" refers to the different species of poultry) such as chicken, turkey, duck, geese, guineas and pigeon, and the various classes within each kind. Of the kinds of poultry, chicken is the most popular.
4. Classes of Poultry:
    a. The various classes of chickens are Rock Cornish game hen, broiler or fryer, roaster, capon hen or baking chicken; stag, cock or rooster.
    b. The various classes of turkeys are fryer/roaster turkey, young turkey, yearling hen or tom turkey, mature or old turkey (hen or tom).

D. Standards (Specifications) of Quality for Dressed and Ready-to-cook Poultry.

1. There are eight specifications of quality which serve as criteria in determining consumer grades of poultry. These are conformation, fleshing, fat covering, pinfeathers, exposed flesh, discolorations, disjointed and broken bones, and freezing defects. These factors are used collectively to evaluate and determine grade of the bird.
2. Quality grading of poultry is based primarily on the visual appearance of the dressed bird. Unlike the red meat species (where there is wide variation in muscling, fatness and quality) poultry has been genetically selected for carcass uniformity. Because body composition is so similar, visual appearance is given ultimate importance in grading. In other words, certain minimum requirements and maximum defects of a carcass are permitted within each grade. US Grade A has the highest requirements and the least defects. About 85 percent of broilers are graded U.S. Grade A. Lower grade (U.S. Grades B or C) are given to birds as they exceed the minimum requirements and/(or) maximum defects per grade.

3. The description of a US Grade A bird is:
    a.   Conformation is nearly normal in all respects so as not to detract from appearance or affect the normal distribution of flesh
    b. Fleshing is well developed
    c. Fat covering is well developed and uniformly distributed
    d. Pinfeathers are absent
    e. Exposed flesh is absent on the breasts and legs and is allowed at a minimum on other parts
    f. Discoloration of the skin and flesh are practically free of such defects
    g. Disjointed or broken bones are absent, and 8. Frozen birds, or parts thereof are practically free from defects that may occur as a result of handling, freezing and storing.

D. Chicken Fabrication: Consumers may purchase chicken as whole, halves, quarters or parts. Today, however, much of the chicken found in the retail store is packaged in parts. These parts can be packaged as white meat (breasts), dark meat (legs and thighs) or mixed according to consumer demand.

1. One way of cutting a chicken into parts is as follows:
    a. Cut the chicken in half by opening the back and splitting along either side of the backbone. The halves can be quartered by cutting midway between the leg, wing, and at a right angle to the backbone.
    b. Remove the wing.
    c. Remove the leg.
    d. Remove the tail piece.
    e. Separate the rib and neck piece from the breast.
    f. Divide the breast into three parts: two half breasts and a wishbone breast.
2. Chicken Cuts
    a. Breasts (Figure 27) and Wishbones
        1. Breasts are cut from the back at the junction of the vertebral and sternal ribs. Ribs may or may not be removed and the breasts may be separated along the breastbone into halves.
        2. A wishbone (Figure 27) may be produced by cutting it from the breast midway between the front point of the breastbone and the end of the wishbone (clavicle) to a point where the wishbone joins the shoulder.
    b. Wings (Figure 27) include the entire wing (humerus, radius, ulna, and metacarpus) with all muscle and skin intact. The wing tip (phalanges) may be removed.

    c. Legs or Drumsticks (Figure 27) and Thighs (Figure 27)
        1. Legs include thighs (femur) and drumsticks (tibia), and are removed by disjointing the thigh at the hip joint (may include pelvic meat but not pelvic bones.)
    d. Backs are those cuts containing the pelvic bones and all the vertebrae posterior to the shoulder joint. It may be cut into two parts (front and back halves).
    e. Necks are cuts with skin and are removed at the last cervical vertebra.

F.   A high proportion of chicken products are further processed.
        1. Broiler meat is an inexpensive protein ingredient in many different processed meat products. Whole muscle cuts are conveniently marinated, or brined. Whole muscle cuts such as breasts and thighs also can be easily seasoned, fully cooked, frozen and then packaged for the home or restaurant market. Trimmings from the fabrication process and mechanically separated meat are convenient, inexpensive protein sources in sausage products and in sectioned and formed products.
        2. Most turkeys are fabricated in the processing plant and only a small fraction remain as intact birds for familiar holiday celebrations. Whole turkey breasts are a lean source of high quality protein and are sold as brined fresh or fully cooked in some other form for sandwiches. Thigh meat, drumsticks, wings and necks are darker and are a common ingredients in turkey sausages and hams.

Figure 26. Skeleton of chicken with parts and bones identified.

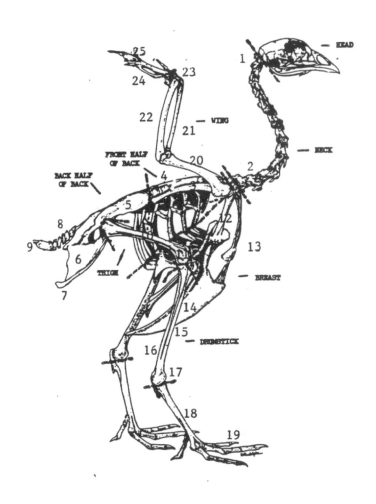

Parts are identified by broken lines and bones are identified by number: (1) first cervical vertebra (atlas) (2) last cervical vertebra, (3) scapula, (4) fused thoracic vertebrae, (5) ilium, (6) ischium, (7) pubis, (8) coccygeal vertebrae, (9) pygostyle, (10) femur, (11) patella, (12) coracoid, (13) clavicle, (14) sternum, (15) fibula, (16) tibia, (17) sesamoid, (18) metatarsus, (19) bones of toes (phalanges), (20) humerus, (21) radius, (22) ulna, (23) carpal bones, (24) metacarpus and, (25) finger bones (phalanges).

Figure 27. Retail cuts of chicken.

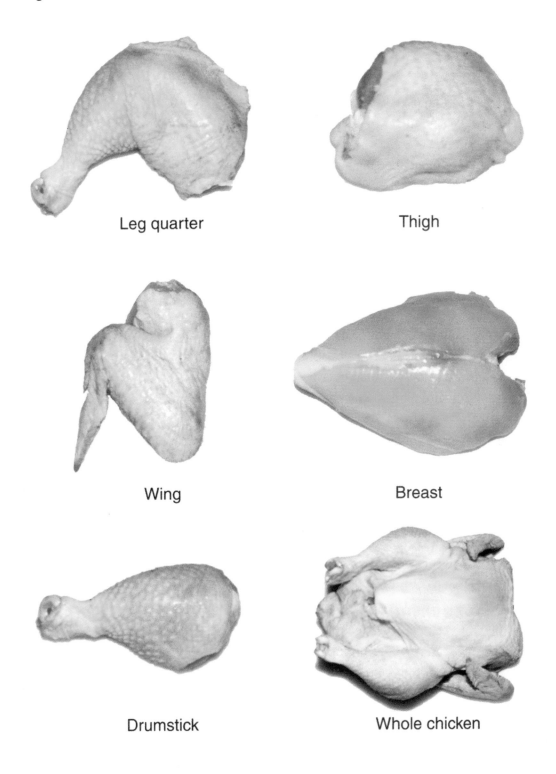

Leg quarter

Thigh

Wing

Breast

Drumstick

Whole chicken

IX. MEAT COOKERY METHODS

A. Dry Heat Method - This method is used for tender cuts of meat or for less tender marinated cuts. Dry heat methods include broiling, roasting, pan-broiling, pan-frying and stir-frying.

1. Broiling
   a. Steaks or chops on a grill or broiler pan are directly exposed to heat in an oven or on an outdoor grill. If an oven is used set the regulator on broil (this is about 400°F).
   b. Place 1 inch steaks, chops or patties 2 to 3 inches from heat and 3 to 5 inches from heat for thicker cuts.
   c. When brown, turn meat and finish to desired degree of doneness.
   d. The three degrees of doneness, their corresponding internal temperature and internal and external color are:
      1. Rare 140° F Red to pink center slightly brown on the outside
      2. Medium 160° F Slight pink center and brown on outside
      3. Well Done 170° F Brown center and dark brown outside

2. Grilling
   a. This method is a form of broiling and it is a very popular way to cook tender cuts as well as ground and processed meats. Also, grilling is often used to cook kabobs, a combination of pieces of meat, vegetables and fruits alternately placed on a skewer. Meat products are usually grilled over heated charcoal and ceramic briquettes and open fires. While direct heat is most common, indirect heat can be used for grilling.

3. Barbeque
   a. Barbeque consists of cooking at low temperatures for a long period of time to impart its characteristic sensory qualities. The low temperature approach makes it ideal for cuts with a high proportion of connective tissue. Pork spare ribs, pork back ribs, pork shoulders, beef brisket, beef tri-tip, beef short ribs, and chicken are all popular barbeque items. Wood smoke and an indirect heat source are key parts of a successful product.

4. Roasting
   a. Season with salt, pepper, etc as desired. Then place the meat in an open roasting pan on a rack with the fat side up.
   b. Do not add water, cover or baste.
   c. Roast in a slow oven (325° F) until cooked to the desired degree of doneness as shown on a meat thermometer.
   d. The use of a meat thermometer is essential for cooking palatable roasts.

5. Pan-broiling
   a. Meat is placed in a heavy frying pan.
   b. Do not add fat or water, and do not cover.
   c. Cook slowly, turning occasionally.
   d. Pour fat from pan as it accumulates.

  e. Brown meat on both sides, then cook to desired degree of doneness and season if desired.
6. Pan-frying
  a. Place meat in heavy frying pan and brown meat on both sides in a small amount of fat.
  b. Season with salt, pepper, etc. as desired.
  c. Do not cover.
  d. Cook at moderate temperature until desired doneness, turning occasionally.
7. Stir-frying
  a. Stir frying is similar to pan-frying except thin slices of meat and vegetables are first cooked separately and then combined.
  b. The combined meat and vegetable are cooked in a wok or large frying pan containing a small amount of oil at high temperatures with almost continuous stirring.

B. Moist Heat Methods - This method is employed for less tender cuts of meat

1. Braising
  a. Moisture is added so as to more readily break down connective tissue during cooking thus making the cuts increase in tenderness. The cooking liquids make gravies as the water-soluble flavor ingredients are cooked out of the meat. Brown meat on all sides in fat in a heavy utensil.
  b. Season with salt, pepper, etc. as desired.
  c. Add a small quantity of liquid (water, soup stock, milk, etc.)
  d. Cover tightly.
  e. Cook at low temperature until tender.
2. Cooking in Liquid (simmering and stewing)
  a. Brown meat on all sides and season as desired.
  b. Cover meat with liquid, cover cooking pan and cook below boiling point (simmer, 185° F to 205°F) until tender.
  c. Stewing is similar to simmering, but stewing uses small pieces f meat whereas simmering uses large pieces of meat.

C. Deep fat frying is cooking meat immersed in fat or oil. Breaded and battered chicken parts and pork tenderloins are examples of delicious tender products used in deep fat frying cookery.

D. Microwave cookery uses radiant energy to cause rapid movement of water within the meat and create heat to cook the product. There are advantages and disadvantages of microwave cookery. It is an excellent way to cook processed products like bacon and ham slices, and reheat precooked meats. Lack of uniform heating and the absence of conventional cooked meat flavors can be disadvantages. The use of microwave cookery is becoming very popular. Consequently, manufacturers, meat promotion groups and others have developed cookbooks for the preparation of meat cuts.

E. Although visual observation of external and internal color is used to gauge doneness of a meat product, the use of meat thermometer is preferred. Figure 27 has illustrations of six degrees of doneness of broiled beef loin steaks. For example, steak broiled to a rare degree of doneness (geometric center of 140° F, = 60° C) has a reddish pink center and slightly brown exterior. A steak broiled to a medium rare degree of doneness (geometric center of 150° F, = 65° C) has a slightly reddish pink interior and a slightly brown external surface. A steak broiled to a medium degree of doneness (geometric center of 160° F, = 70° C) has a slightly pink interior and a brown exterior. And a steak broiled to a well done degree of doneness (geometric center of 170° F, = 75° C) has a brown center and a dark brown to slightly charred external surface.

F. Figure 28 illustrates the various degrees of doneness based on color. From a food safety degree of doneness, the juices on the surface of the patty should run clear when cooking, and a brown center should be evident. In ground beef, the cooked colors can be misleading, thus the importance of using a meat thermometer to cook to 160° F.

Figure 28. Illustrations of different degrees of doneness of cooked beef steaks.

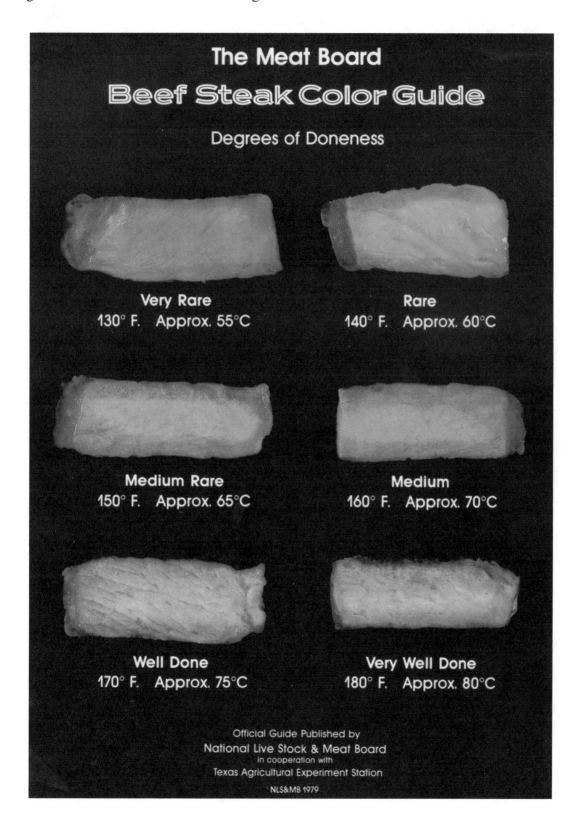

Figure 29. Illustrations of degrees of doneness of cooked ground beef patties.

X.   FRANKFURTER MANUFACTURE

A.   General

Frankfurters are classified as cooked and smoked sausages. Frankfurters are a blend of finely chopped beef, pork, and/or poultry meat, cured, mildly seasoned, stuffed in peelable cellulose casings, smoked and cooked, and then refrigerated. For "old world taste" frankfurters are stuffed in lamb small intestine casings. These casings are edible. Frankfurters, franks, wieners and hot dogs are synonymous names. Cocktail franks are smaller than regular franks and serve as appetizers, and Vienna-style frankfurters are cooked and canned. Most frankfurters are sold skinless (cellulose casing removed), and the most popular size is 1.6 ounces, or 10 to a pound. Today, a large percentage of frankfurters are manufactured from poultry meat. The use of poultry or poultry combined with red meats allows lower production costs.

Thirty percent fat is the legal limit allowed in the production of frankfurters. Today, however, many manufacturers are producing low fat frankfurters, less than 10 percent fat, and some are fat-free lean.

Frankfurters are made from finely comminuted meat batters. This requires the use of a piece of equipment called a bowl chopper. Bowl choppers have rapidly moving blades to reduce meat and fat particles to very small sizes. The addition of salt and water to the lean meat is important for the formation of an emulsion. Lean meat is always introduced first so that salt and chopping extract salt soluble proteins. After extraction of the salt soluble proteins, the fat trim is added to the chopper.

Salt soluble meat proteins function to encapsulate the fat particles and bind water. A stable batter is the goal of the manufacturer for supplying quality products for retail sale. Quality control measures prevent these kinds of products (separation of fat and lean) from getting into the retail store.

Although frankfurters are fully cooked, they must be refrigerated. Hot dogs can be boiled, grilled, fried, broiled, barbecued and microwaved.

B.	Manufacturing procedure

1.	In formulating a high quality frank, 90 percent lean cow meat and 50 percent pork trim are used in equal proportions.

2.	Grinding the lean meat is the first step in the production of frankfurters and this may vary depending on processors. A 1/2 to 3/8 inch grinder plate is adequate

3	The ground lean meat is placed in the bowl of the chopper. Salt, curing ingredients, and one-half of the water (ice) is added. Chop to a temperature of 42-45°F before the remaining water, fat meat and spices are added. After adding these ingredients, chopping continues until a temperature of 50-56°F is obtained, usually under a vacuum. If non-meat ingredients like cereal flours and non-fat dry milk are added, they should be added near the end of chopping.

4	Stuffing the batter into peelable cellulose casings is accomplished by using a vacuum stuffer and auto-linking device. Otherwise, cellulose and natural casings may be linked manually. After stuffing, frankfurters are suspended from metal rods, (commonly called smoke sticks) on a smokehouse truck.

5.	In the thermal processing unit, the product is dried, smoked, and fully cooked. A typical thermal processing schedule for frankfurters is as follows:

Time	Temperature	% Relative Humidity	Function	Damper
30 min	125°F	25	drying	open
60 min	140°F	35	smoking	closed
60 min	165°F	35	cooking	closed
10 min	180°F	100	steam cooking	closed

6.	Frankfurters are chilled to 36°C or less in a cooler overnight, or in commercial process chilling can be accomplished in about 10 minutes using a 60 percent brine solution refrigerated at about 28°F.

7.	Casings are removed by a mechanical peeler. Steam loosens the casing, and the knife edge cuts the moistened casing as the links move through the machine. An air jet helps in the removal of the casing by blowing it off the frankfurters. In excess of 5000 lb per hour can be peeled by using high speed peelers under commercial conditions. Franks are vacuum packaged and refrigerated until cooked for consumption.

C. A typical formulation for frankfurters is as listed:

Ingredient	Amount
90:10 lean beef (90% lean)	50 lb
50:50 pork trim (50% lean)	50 lb
Ice	20 lb
Salt	2.8 lb
Sodium nitrite	1/4 oz
Sodium erythroblast	7/8 oz
Sugar	1 lb
White pepper	1/4 oz
Nutmeg	2 oz
Ginger	2 oz
Onion powder	1 oz

XI. FRESH BRATWURST MANUFACTURE

A.   General

Fresh bratwurst is a coarse or fine ground pork combined with various seasonings and stuffed into edible collagen or natural hog casings. Three percent added water is allowed in fresh sausage. Most commercial varieties will vary from 25 to 40% fat.

B.   A typical manufacturing procedure is as follows:

1.   In formulating a bratwurst, 60 lb of 80 pork trim and 40 lb of 50 pork trim is recommended.

2.   The pork is ground through a 3/8" grinder plate. The meat should be at 28-32^{0}F to minimize "smearing" of the product

3.   The ground meat is mixed with a salt/spice premix.

4.   All ingredients are ground through a 1/8" grinder plate.

5.   The mixture is then stuffed into 28-30 mm collagen casing or a natural casing using a stuffer.

6.   Links can be made by using an auto-linker or can be linked by hand.

7.   Links are then packaged and refrigerated or frozen.

C.   A typical formulation for bratwurst is as follows:

Ingredients	Amount
80:20 pork trim (80% lean)	60 lb
50:50 pork trim (50% lean)	40 lb
Salt	2 lb
Sugar	4 oz
Black pepper	5 oz
Sage	3.5 oz
Ginger	2.5 oz
White pepper	2 oz
Coriander (lemon-like flavor)	0.7 oz
Nutmeg (sweet, warm)	0.7 oz
Ground celery seed	0.6 oz
Caraway (warm, slightly sharp)	0.6 oz
Cardamon (pleasant, warm)	0.6 oz
Savory (fragrant, aromatic)	0.25 oz

XII. SUMMER SAUSAGE MANUFACTURE

A.   General

Summer sausage is a term used to encompass a family of semi-dry and dry fermented
sausages. Consequently, the use of the term summer sausage makes accurate
identification of these kinds of sausages confusing at best. Cervelats, salamis and
thuringers are members of the summer sausage family. Cervelats and thuringers
are more mildly seasoned and have a softer consistency than salamis. Salamis
have a harder, firmer texture because they are drier. The dried varieties of summer
sausages can be stored preserved refrigeration because of low pH and moisture
and high salt content which, in combination, inhibit the growth of spoilage
bacteria. The low pH can be achieved with fermentation with lactic acid
producing bacteria or with encapsulated acids. On the other hand, semi-dry
sausages, although having a low pH, have a higher moisture content and must be
refrigerated.

Summer sausage is a generic term to describe sausage made usually of equal parts of
beef and pork, although there may be all beef summer sausage. The meat
ingredients are coarsely chopped, mildly seasoned, fermented and stuffed into
inedible fibrous casings.

The key to an excellent summer sausage is controlled bacterial fermentation of the
sausage during processing. This is best accomplished by using a commercial
preparation of a lactic acid starter culture. Bacterial fermentation lowers the pH
(typical range is 4.6-5.4), and gives the product its tangy flavor by producing lactic
acid from added dextrose. The lower the pH, the tangier the flavor. Some
consumers like a very tangy flavor and others like a more mild tanginess. With a
commercial starter culture preparation and with dextrose addition, flavor can be
controlled. Starter cultures usually consist of a blend of two or more
microorganisms. The more commonly used ones are <u>Pediococcus,</u> <u>Micrococcus</u>
and <u>Lactobacillus</u>.

B.   Process

1.   A high quality summer sausage consists of 1) 50:50 pork trim and 90:10 beef trim, or 2) 90:10 boneless cow meat, 75:25 beef trim, and 50:50 beef trim. Summer sausage may be a combination of pork and beef, or may be all beef.

2.   Grind meat through a 3/8" grinder plate. Meat should be well chilled (28-32^0F). Well-chilled meat when ground will have a "smoother" cleaner particle definition in the finished product.

3.   Mix meat thoroughly with the spices for 3-4 minutes.

4.   Add a commercial starter culture preparation, and mix for an additional 3-4 minutes.

5.   The mixture is ground through a 1/8 inch grinder plate.

6.   The mixture is stuffed by using a Vemag stuffer into 2 inch diameter fibrous casings and clipped.

7.   The product is hung on smoke sticks and placed in the thermal processor unit. In the first phase of the thermal processing schedule, fermentation takes place as the low temperature stimulates the lactic acid starter culture to breakdown dextrose to lactic acid. Thereafter, the product is smoked and cooked. Thermal processing is as follows:

Time	Temperature	% Relative Humidity	Function
8-12 hr	85-100°F	75-85	Fermentation (pH drops to 4.6)
1-2 hr (near end of fermentation)	85-100°F	75-85	Smoke
1.5-3 hr	155°F	60	Cook
148^{0}F internal	165°F	45	Final cook
3 min			Cold shower to chill

8.   Refrigerate

C. A typical formulation for summer sausage is as follows:

Ingredient	Amount
50:50 pork trim	50 lbs
90:10 beef trim	50 lbs
Salt	3 lbs
Dextrose	2 lbs
Coarse ground black pepper	6 oz
Fine ground black pepper	1 oz
Whole mustard seed	1/2 oz
Nutmeg	2 oz
Coriander	1/2 oz
Allspice (pungent, clove-like)	1/2 oz
Sodium nitrite	1/4 oz

Lactic acid starter culture. Follow manufacturer's recommendation.

XIII. MEATS USED IN SAUSAGE MANUFACTURE

(Classified according to binding* qualities)

A. Meats having best binding qualities are:
1. Hot bull beef
2. Chilled bull beef
3. Beef shank meat
4. Beef chucks
5. Boneless cow meat

B. Meats having fairly good binding qualities are:
1. Beef head meat
2. Beef cheeks
3. Boneless veal
4. Calf head meat
5. Pork trimmings, extra lean
6. Pork trimmings, lean
7. Pork head meat
8. Pork cheeks

C. Meats having poor binding qualities are:
1. Beef hearts
2. Beef weasand meat
3. Beef giblets
4. Beef tongue trimmings
5. Regular pork trimmings
6. Pork hearts
7. Pork jowls
8. Pork ham fat
9. Sheep cheeks
10. Sheep hearts

D. The following meats, while nutritious, have practically no binding qualities at all and are used as fillers in the interest of economy. The use of these ingredients should be limited to less than 25 percent of the meat formula because of their high connective tissue content.
1. Ox lips
2. Beef tripe
3. Pork snouts
4. Pork lips
5. Pork tripe

*Bind is defined as the capacity to attract and retain water and encapsulated fat.

XIV. EXAMPLES OF NATURAL AND SYNTHETIC CASINGS
Used for Various Kinds of Sausage Products

A. Natural Casings
- 1. Pork Casings   <u>Packaged Product</u>
  - a. Hog Bungs   Braunschweiger
  - b. Middles (middle portion of large intestine)   Dry Sausage
  - c. Small Casings (small intestine)   Frankfurters
  - d. Stomachs   Head Cheese
  - e. Bladders   Minced Luncheon Meat
- 2. Beef Casings
  - a. Middles (Large intestine)   Cervelat, Salami
  - b. Rounds (small intestine)   Bologna
  - c. Bungs (trade name cecum)   Berliner, Cappicola
  - d. Weasands (Lining of esophagus)   Long Bologna
  - e. Bladders   Luncheon Meat
- 3. Sheep Casings
  - a. Middle (Large intestine)   Frankfurters
  - b. Small (Small intestine)   Frankfurters

B. Synthetic Casings
- 1. Type of casing   <u>Packaged Product</u>
  - a. Cellulose   Frankfurters
  - b. Plastic   Braunschweiger
  - c. Fibrous   Summer Sausages; Bologna

XV. VARIETY MEATS AND OTHER MEATS

This table contains a list of variety meats (internal) and other meats (external). These meats are usually economical and some supply excellent dietary sources of vitamins and minerals, especially liver. Many of these products are enjoyed, however, by only certain geographical and ethnic groups. Because we in the U.S. do not consume large quantities of these meats, we are fortunate to have an excellent export trade for these variety and other meats.

VARIETY MEATS
(Internal)

BEEF

Beef Brains	Beef Sweetbreads
Beef Heart	Beef Tongue
Beef Kidney	Smoked Beef
Tongue	
Beef Liver	Beef Tripe
Beef Liver Sliced	Beef Fries

PORK

Pork Brains	Pork Kidney
Pork Cheeks	Pork Liver
Pork Chitterlings	Pork Liver Sliced
Pork Fries	Pork Tongue
Pork Hearts	

LAMB

Lamb Fries	Lamb Liver
Lamb Hearts	Lamb Liver Sliced
Lamb Kidneys	Lamb Tongue

VEAL

Veal Brains	Veal Liver Sliced
Veal Heart	Veal Sweetbreads
Veal Kidneys	Veal Tongue
Veal Liver	Calf Fries

OTHER MEATS
(External)

BEEF

Beef Ox Tails	Beef Suet

PORK

Pigs Feet	Pork Lips
Pork Blade Bones	Pork Skin
Pork Breast Bones	Pork Snouts
Pork Cracklings	Pork Tails
Pork Ears	Smoked Pork
Pork Fat Back	Pork Neckbones
Pork Head	Salt Fat Back
Pork Jowl	Salt Pork
Pork Leaf Fat	Salt Side

VEAL

Calf Feet	Calf Head

XVI. PORCINE MUSCLE AND BONE IDENTIFICATION

Although the muscles and bones identified on these pages are for pork, the basically apply to all red meat species. Knowledge and identification of muscles and bones are keys to retail meat cut recognition.

Figure 30.   Location and identification letters of cross sections from the porcine carcass.

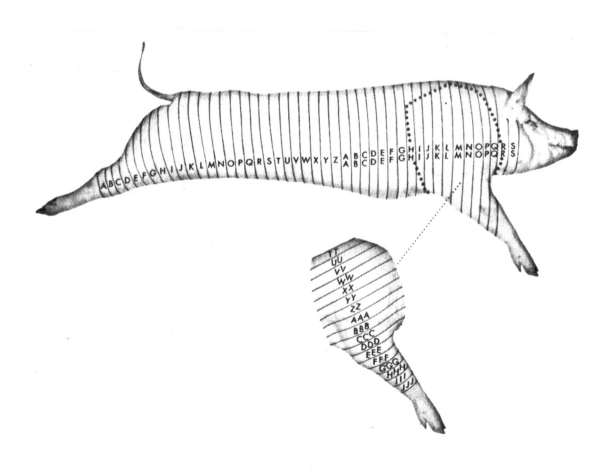

Figure 31.

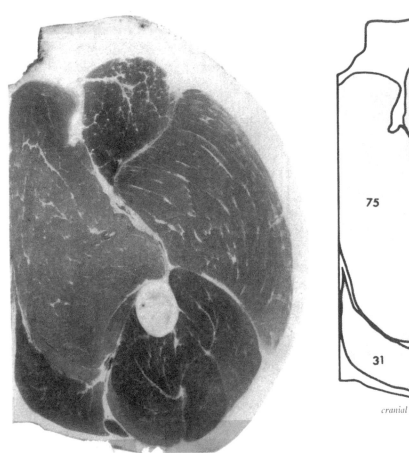 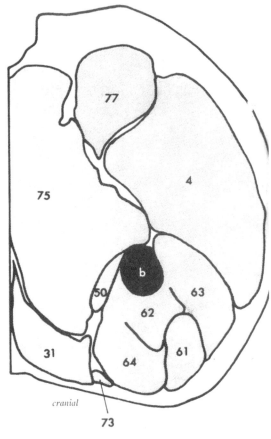

Typical Retail Cuts:

Center ham slice (pork)
Round steak (beef)
Top round steak (beef- semimembranosus)
Bottom round steak (beef- biceps femoris)
    intermedius
Eye of the round steak
    (beef-semitendinosus)
Sirloin tip of beef (quadriceps)

Muscles and Bones:

4. Biceps Femoris
31. Gracilus
61. Quadriceps femoris, rectus femoris
62. Quadriceps femoris, vastus

63. Quadricpes femoris, vastus lateralis
64. Quardriceps femoris, vastus medialis
75. Semimembranosus
77. Semitendinosus
b. Femur

Figure 32.

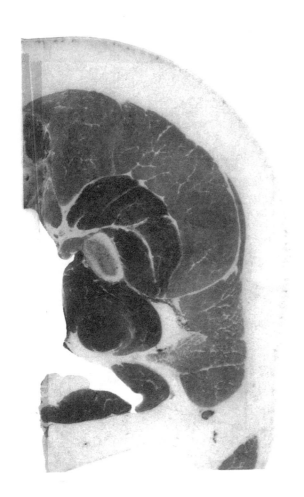 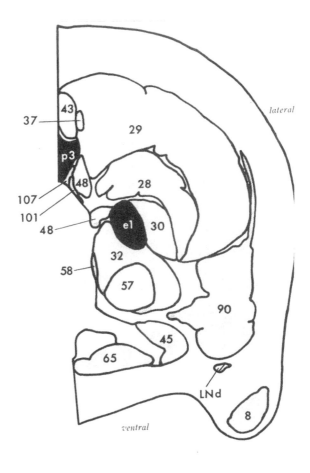

Typical Retail Cuts:
Round bone sirloin steak (beef)
Sirloin chop of pork and lamb
Top sirloin teak (beef-gluteus medius)

Muscles and Bones:
28. Gluteus accessories
29. Gluteus medius
30. Gluteus profundus
32. Illiacus
57. Psoas major
65. Rectus abdominis
90. Tensor fasciae latae
p3. Vertebrae, sacral
e1. Ilium

Figure 33.

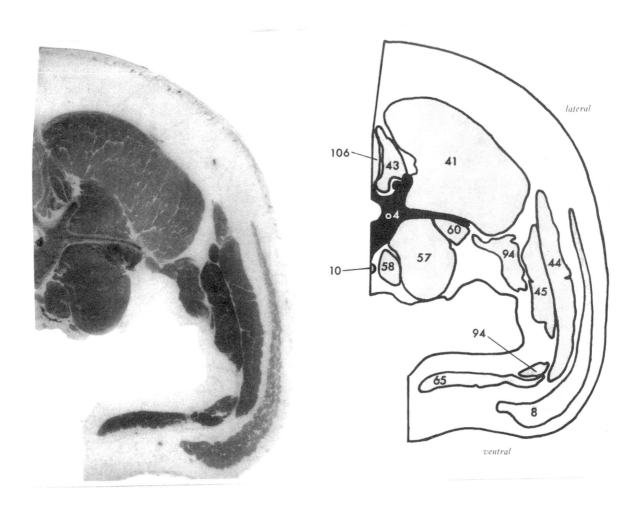

Typical Retail Cuts:
Loin chops of pork and lamb
Porterhouse steak (beef)
Tenderloin (pork) and
     filet mignon (beef-psoas major)
Sliced bacon (muscles 8, 44, 45, 65, 94)

Muscles and Bones:
 8. Cutaneus trunci
41. Longissimus lumborum
43. Multifidus
44. Obliquus abdominis
45. Obliquus intermus abdominis
57. Psoas major
58. Psoas minor
65. Rectus abdominis
94. Transversus abdominus
o4. Vertebrae, lumbar

Figure 34.

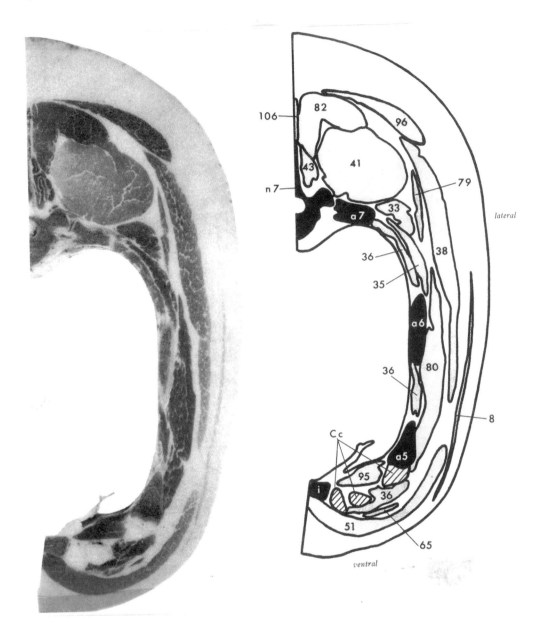

Typical Retail Cuts:
Rib steak (beef)
Rib chop of pork and lamb
Sliced bacon (muscles 38, 51,
      and 80 plus others in this area)

Muscles and Bones:
38. Latissimus dorsi
41. Longissimus thoracis
43. Mutlifidus dorsi
51. Pectoralis profundi
80. Serratus ventralis
82. Spinalis dorsi
96. Trapezius
n7. Thoracic vertebrae
a5, a6, a7. Costae

Figure 35.

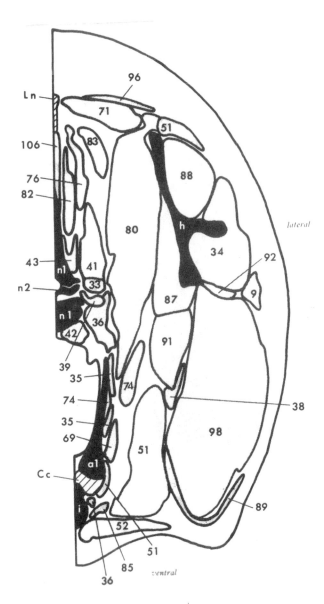

Typical retail Cuts:
Blade chop of pork and lamb
Shoulder roast (lamb)
7-bone chuck steak (beef)
Blade steak of pork
Whole pork shoulder
Boston but (dorsal or top
     portion to include scapula)
Picnic shoulder (portion 1 inch
     ventral to scapula)

Muscles and Bones:
34. Infraspinatus
38. Latissimus dorsi
51. Pectoralis profundi
52. Pectoralis superficiales
80. Serratus ventralis
88. Supraspinatus
96. Trapezius
h. Scapula

Figure 36.

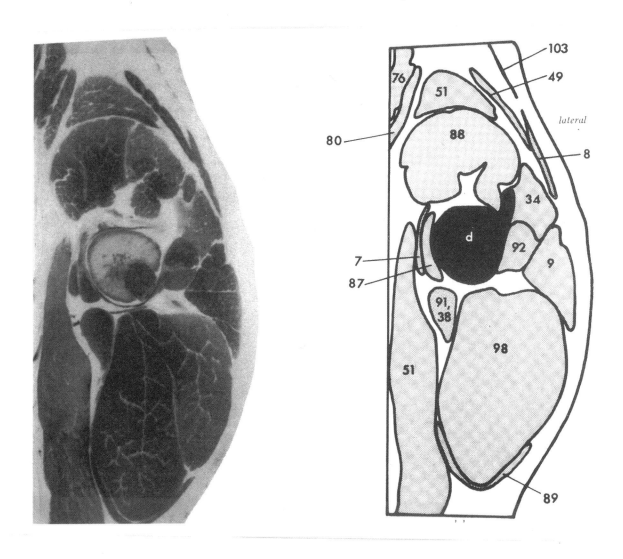

Typical Retail Cuts:
Arm chops of pork and lamb
Arm steak or roast (beef)
Fresh or smoked arm picnic

Muscles and Bones:
51. Pectoralis profundi
88. Biceps brachii
98. Triceps brachii
d. Humerus